NVQ Engineering
Level 2

Mechanical Units

NVQ Engineering
Level 2

Mechanical Units

David Salmon
Lecturer, Royal Forest of Dean College

LONGMAN

Addison Wesley Longman Limited
Edinburgh Gate, Harlow
Essex CM20 2JE, England
and Associated Companies throughout the world

First published 1998

British Library Cataloguing in Publication Data
A catalogue entry for this title is available from the British Library

ISBN 0-582-30299-4

Set by 24 in Garamond 10/12 and Univers
Produced by Addison Wesley Longman Singapore (Pte) Ltd.,
Printed in Singapore

Contents

Preface viii
Acknowledgements viii

1   Safe working practices   1

Safety precautions and procedures to be followed at all times   1
Protective clothing and equipment   2
Personal hygiene procedures   4
Keeping the work area clean and tidy   4
Good working practices   5

2   Basic bench fitting   6

Bench and vice   7
Files and filing   8
  File handles   8
  Selection of file   8
  Using files   10
Hacksaws   16
  Selecting the hacksaws blade   16
  Using hacksaws   17
Drilling on the bench drilling machine   18
  Bench drilling machine   18
  Setting the spindle speed   19
  Work holding   19
  Drilling the hole   19
Hole-cutting tools   22
  Drills   22
  Reamers   23
  Hole-forming tools   24
  Tool-forming devices used in drilling machines   24
The pillar drilling machine   25
  Features of the pillar drill   25
  Using a pillar drill   26
Cutting internal threads   29
  Hand taps   30
  Tap wrenches   30
  Using taps to cut internal threads   30
  Care of taps   31
Cutting external screw threads   31
  Types of die used for hand thread cutting   32
  Die stocks   32
  Using dies to cut external threads   32
  Care of dies   33
Shaping machine   36
Reaming   39
  Hand reaming   40
  Machine reaming   40
Screwdrivers   43
  Selection of screwdrivers   43
  Hexagon socket wrenches (allen keys)   44

Spanners 44
  C-spanner 45
  Engineer's socket set 45
  Torque wrenches 45
Pliers 47
  Selection of pliers 47
  Using pliers 47
Pipe wrench (stillson) 48
Hammers 51
  Riveting 51
Cold chisels 54
  Types of chisel 54
  Using chisels 54
  Grinding chisel points 54

3   Basic centre lathe turning   59

The centre lathe 59
Mounting the work in a three-jaw self-centering chuck 63
Selection of spindle speeds 64
Lathe cutting tool shapes 64
Machine centres 65
Setting the cutting tool in the tool post 66
  Setting the cutting tool in centre 66
Selecting a feed rate 67
Coolant and cutting fluid 67
Positioning of centre lathe guards 67
Operating the centre lathe 68
Thread cutting using dies 72
  Cutting external threads on a centre lathe using dies 72
Facing to length 75
Chamfering 75
Lathe tool materials 76
Angles on lathe cutting tools 76
Defects on centre lathe cutting tools 77
Mounting cutting tools in the tailstock 78
Work-holding devices 82
  Changing the work-holding device 84
Turning between centres 84
Taper turning using the compound slide 86
Boring on a centre lathe 90
  Boring 91
The mandrel 93
  Mounting a workpiece on a mandrel 93
Knurling 97
  Method of using the caliper type knurling tool 97
Tapping 98
  Tapping on a centre lathe by hand 98
  Machine tapping on a centre lathe 99
Parting off 100
Setting work in a four-jaw chuck with a dial test indicator 104
  Setting a workpiece in a four-jaw chuck 104

4   Basic milling   109

The vertical milling machine 110
  Milling techniques used on vertical milling machines 112

Work-holding using a vice   112
   The plain machine vice   113
   The swivelling machine vice   113
   Tilting and swivelling machine vice   113
   Pull-down vice jaws   114
Setting a vice square in a milling machine's table   114
Mounting workpieces in a vice   115
Selection of milling cutters for vertical milling   116
   End mill   116
   Slot drill   116
   Shell end mill   116
   Face mills   117
Mounting a chuck in a vertical milling machine   117
Mounting the cutter in a vertical milling machine   117
   Assembly instructions for mounting end mills or slot drills in a milling chuck   118
Selection of spindle speeds for milling   118
Selecting feed rate   118
Direction of feed   119
Positioning of guards   119
Operating the vertical milling machine   120
Cutting angular faces   124
   Setting a workpiece in a rigid machine vice inclined at an angle   124
   Setting a workpiece in a swivelling vice turned at the required angle   125
   Machining angular workpieces   125
Slot drilling   126
Horizontal milling machines   130
Work-holding in a horizontal milling machine   132
Selection of cutters for horizontal milling   132
   Plain milling cutters   132
   Form relieved cutters   132
   Chuck and stub arbor-mounted cutters   134
Fitting arbor-mounted cutters in a horizontal milling machine   134
Mounting arbors and cutters on a horizontal milling machine   135
Positioning guards   136
Stub arbor   139
   To fit a stub arbor or chuck in a horizontal milling machine   139
Straddle milling   141
   Setting up and straddle milling   141
Defects on milling cutters   144
Other work-holding devices for use on milling machines   145
Vertical milling attachment for horizontal milling machine   148

Appendices
Appendix I   Millimetre to inch conversions   152
Appendix II   Inch to millimetre conversions   153
Appendix III   Tapping sizes for common threads   154
Appendix IV   Drilling speeds and feeds   155
Appendix V   Reaming allowances   156
Appendix VI   Torque wrench settings   157
Appendix VII Spindle speeds for turning and milling   158
Apendix VIII Feed rates for milling   159
Appendix IX   Repeat test   160

Index   161

Preface

This workbook, together with two complementary titles (covering the mandatory units and the electrical option units) have been written for people working towards an Engineering NVQ Level 2 qualification. The books contain information about all the required skills underpinning knowledge and a series of exercises which meet the course objectives. By completing the exercises at the trainee's own pace he/she will generate an evidence portfolio for the NVQ 2 Engineering award.

With the pressure on college lecturers and the relative inexperience of some industrial trainers new to this type of work in mind, the books were devised to afford minimum inconvenience in the setting up and running of a study programme for engineering trainees. However, it must be recognised that practical skills can only be learned through high quality instruction from suitably qualified teachers who demonstrate the procedures, and who advise and supervise trainees to ensure that safe practices are observed. Trainees should follow up this instruction with plenty of practice.

A qualified assessor should approve each exercise on its completion. When the book is satisfactorily completed, a qualification can be applied for.

The exercises within the book are valuable for anyone wishing to practise mechanical engineering skills on any training course. Included at the end of the book is reference material in an appendix which I hope will be useful throughout a trainee's engineering career.

David Salmon
1998

Note to lecturers

There is an accompanying tutor's manual for this book which contains guidance on using the book, along with multiple choice tests, with answers, for each chapter. This manual is available, in hardcopy and electronic format, to all bone fide lecturers adopting this book for a course of twelve or more students. Please contact the FE Marketing Department on 01279 623437 for details of how to obtain your copy.

Acknowledgements

The author and publisher are grateful to the following companies for their help during the preparation of this text, and for permission to reproduce copyright materials:

Bridgeport Machines Limited	Moore & Wright
Britool Limited	Nelsa Limited
Cincinnati Milacron UK Limited	Pratt Bernerd International
Clarkson Osborn International	Presto Engineers' Cutting Tools Limited
Colchester Lathe Company	Silvaflame Co. Limited
Dormer Tools Limited	The L. S. Starrett Company Limited
Hattersley Newman Hender Limited	The 600 Group plc
Jacobs' Manufacturing Company	WDS Standard Parts Limited

Thanks also to Mr R. L. Timings for allowing the inclusion of some illustrations from his books and to Mr Geoff Howell for his advice and technical help.

Chapter 1

Safe working practices

Safety is one of the most important elements in the working life of all people. Mechanical engineers work in an environment which can potentially be very dangerous. Only when dangers are recognised and understood can appropriate measures be taken to protect against personal accidental injury, ill health or damage to equipment.

The most important safety law is the Health and Safety at Work Act 1974. It outlines the responsibilities of employers, employees and suppliers of goods. You should be aware of this safety law, particularly Section 2 (General duties of employers to their employees) and Section 7 (General duties of employees at work). You should also be aware that there is a person appointed to look after safety issues, usually called the Safety Officer. However for information on safety issues, you would normally refer to your supervisor in the first instance.

As you work through this book you must work safely. All the exercises require you to use safe working practices, so you must know what this means and how to behave. The following safety rules have been set out for your guidance. Remember that there may be special rules in your workplace, and that the rules below are for general information. If you follow these rules and heed the warnings, you will significantly reduce your chances of being involved in an accident.

Safety precautions and procedures to be followed at all times

Your behaviour in an engineering workshop must be responsible and appropriate. This means that you **must always** follow these rules:

- Wear safety glasses at all times in the workshop.
- Use protective clothing and equipment.
- Know the emergency stop procedures.
- Follow instructions carefully.
- Be aware of what is going on around you.
- Use appropriate guards on all machine tools.
- Use correct lifting technique.
- Observe safety, warning and prohibition signs which may be posted about the workshop and work areas. They are there for your benefit.
- Observe all workshop rules.
- Ask for help and advice when unsure about anything.

and you **must never**:

- run in the workshop
- smoke in unauthorised areas
- operate a machine without authorisation
- start a machine unless you have been shown how to work it properly
- throw anything
- push persons or get involved in horseplay
- remove a guard from a machine
- distract others operating a machine by asking questions, shouting or making loud noises
- play around with compressed air lines

Protective clothing and equipment

Section 2 of the Health and Safety at Work Act requires employers to provide all necessary safety equipment for any task an employee is asked to do. It is the duty of employees (this is you) to use and look after this equipment correctly in order to conform with Section 7 of the Health and Safety at Work Act 1974. Doing this will lessen the chances of accidents and consequently reduce the chances of personal injury.

Protective clothing used by engineers may include some of the following, depending on the work that is to be carried out:

1. **Overalls**

Overalls are necessary when there are moving parts of machinery and the engineer needs to keep his loose clothing contained to prevent entanglement. Overalls also provide a means of keeping dirt and chemicals off engineer's clothes. As well as these safety uses, overalls can also provide identification and security when used as a type of uniform.

Various styles of overall are in common use:

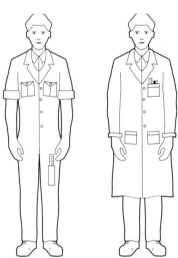

Boiler suit
This gives maximum protection to the wearer and his clothes. It is close fitting and unlikely to become caught in moving machinery.

Coat overall
Comfortable and easy to take on and off. Not sufficiently close fitting to be safe when using machinery. Normally worn by: storemen, inspectors, supervisors, laboratory assistants.

Other types of overall include:

- Bib and braces – dungaree type overalls.
- Two piece – separate jacket and trousers.

2. **Safety boots**

A pair of safety boots made to BS 1870 will have many safety features. The most noticeable feature is steel toecaps. These can protect the toes should a heavy object be dropped onto the foot. Other safety features on some industrial footwear are listed below.

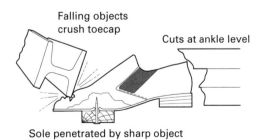

Falling objects crush toecap

Cuts at ankle level

Sole penetrated by sharp object

Lightweight shoe offering no protection

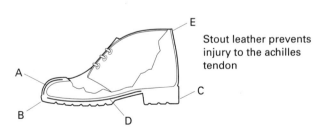

E

Stout leather prevents injury to the achilles tendon

A

C

B

D

An industrial safety boot

A	Steel toe cap	Toe protection against falling objects.
B	Chemical/oil resistant soles	For grip in oily and chemical environments.
C	Non-slip rubber sole	Tread pattern improves grip on smooth surfaces.
D	Steel inner sole	Protects against penetration from underneath.
E	Ankle protection	Helps to avoid injury to achilles tendon.

3. Safety glasses

Various types and styles are available. BS 2092 lenses are suitable for protection against impact from flying debris in an engineering workshop. Safety glasses are to be worn at all times in workshops weather you are operating a machine or not.

Popular style of safety glasses

4. Safety helmet (hard hat)

Wear a safety helmet when working:

(a)   below others as they could drop something
(b)   in places where the ceiling is low or uneven
(c)   where there is scaffolding
(d)   when a sign directs you to do so.

Safety helmet

5. Hats and hair nets

Hats should be worn by all when there is any risk of getting your hair tangled in a rotating tool or workpiece. Some people prefer to use a hair net. The picture shows what can happen if you get the top of your head too close to a rotating drill in a drilling machine.

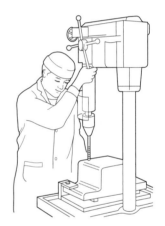

Caught hair in drilling machine

Ear defenders

6. Ear defenders and ear plugs

These are necessary for all those working in areas where loud noise levels exist. Ear defenders look like headphones, ear plugs are smaller and fit inside the ears.

7. Apron

Rubber or polypropylene aprons provide protection against the affects of chemical attack. Never use an apron unless you are sure it will provide protection against the particular chemical you are exposed to. These aprons must be such that they provide appropriate protection for the specific chemical.

8. Dust mask

When working in a dusty environment, an engineer should wear a dust mask to filter the air for his own protection.

9. Respirator

Respirators are face masks which draw a clean supply of air from elsewhere; note the air supply pipe in the drawing. Respirators must be worn when working in poison environments or where fumes and chemicals may leak causing discomfort or illness.

Respirator

10. **Gloves**

Gloves are worn for hand protection. The main types in common use include:

(a) Leather

Leather gloves are tough and flexible, they should be used when handling things that have sharp edges to protect hands against being cut.

(b) Thermal insulation

Gloves offering thermal insulation are made out of leather and lined with an insulation material. Asbestos was used for this insulation years ago, so these gloves are sometimes *wrongly* called 'asbestos gloves'.

(c) Rubber (latex)

Thin rubber (latex) gloves provide protection against the effects of a range of chemicals e.g. salts, detergents and harmful oils. Never use these gloves unless you are sure they will protect you against the chemical you are exposed to.

(a)
Leather gloves – for sharp edges

(b)
Thermal insulation gloves

(c)
Latex gloves for chemical protection

11. **Guards**

All machines are fitted with various types of guards. You must learn how to use guards for each type of machine which *must* be used at all times.

12. **Other specialist protection**

There are other pieces of specialist protective clothing available for those working in hazardous environments. The items of protective equipment described above are the most common, but if you are at all concerned about working in an environment, always ask your supervisor or another responsible person about protective clothing.

Personal hygiene procedures

Wash hands at the end of your work shift and before eating or handling food. This is very important because many products in the workshop, particulary lubricants and oils are harmful irritants and if consumed cause illness. Food and drink should never be brought into an engineering workshop.

Clean your overalls regularly to reduce the chances of oils soaking through the material and becoming in contact with your skin. Oils on your skin can cause a skin disease called dermatitis. Dermatitis particularly affects sensitive skin so always wash your hands before using the toilet. You can minimise the chances of getting dermatitis on your hands by applying protective barrier hand cream – this hand cream should always be applied at the start of any work shift.

Keeping the work area clean and tidy

A tidy workshop is more likely to be a safe workshop. Always keep a look out for mislaid things to trip over and slip on. It is your duty under the Health and Safety at Work Act to report such things or tidy them up. Spilt oil can be tidied up with a mop or covered with sawdust. Gangways and exit routes in particular should be clear of obstacles at all times.

Care when storing and stacking materials is essential since accidents can happen if the materials are lightly knocked. Don't leave things sticking out of shelves.

Take care laying electric power cords so that they do not become 'trip wires'. It is correct to position a sign to inform others of such hazards.

As well as for safety, general workshop tidiness is important because it makes it easy to find equipment.

Good working practices

- Use machine guards at all times.
- Respect others by co-operating.
- Behave responsibly.
- Obey all safety practices and procedures.
- Report all failures of machines and equipment.
- Report all accidents and incidents.
- Remove rings and watches
- Know emergency exit routes and procedures.
- Care for and store tools and equipment properly.
- Get to know the procedures for accident reporting.
- Remember the procedures for first aid and emergency evacuation – you may need them one day.

Above all, it is important to develop safety awareness and be alert at all times.

Notes of special safety rules in my workplace

1.

2.

3.

4.

5.

Chapter 2
Basic bench fitting

Exercise	Page	Date	Signed by Trainer
2.1 Drill drift	13		
2.2 Slot cleaner	20		
2.3 Depth guage body	27		
2.4 Clutch tool handle	34		
2.5 Toolmakers clamp	37		
2.6 Drill stand	41		
2.7 Gate valve	48		
2.8 Drill stand assembly	52		
2.9 Sharpening and using chisels	56		
2.10 Multi-choice test on all work in this chapter	58		

Appropriate safety precautions and procedures regarding risks of personal injury; danger to others and damage to equipment are observed	
The trainee has been observed to wear appropriate protective clothing	
The trainee has been observed to follow personal protection/ hygiene procedures	
The trainee has been observed to keep the work area clean and tidy	
The trainee has been seen to observe Health & Safety requirements and observe good working practices	

The bench fitter is one of the most skilled tradesmen within mechanical engineering. Bench fitting involves using hand tools for hand shaping and fine finishing of components so that they can be assembled with precision. Typical components assembled by fitters include machine parts, measuring devices and work setting fixtures. The fitters' work can also involve hand making individual parts as required. Fitters use simple tools such as files, saws, hammers and punches, they also use light machine tools such as drilling machines and shapers.

The bench fitter is based at a work-bench fitted with a vice and usually has access to a surface plate for marking out workpieces.

The hand skills used in fitting are not easy to acquire and must be practised so that a high level of precision can be achieved. Knowledge of the tools and equipment is necessary so that the right tool can be selected for the job in hand. The following pages describe various hand tools and their uses. There are a series of exercises designed to enable you to demonstrate your skills in selecting and using these tools.

Bench and vice

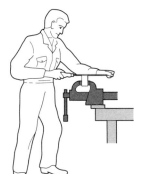

Vice mounted at the correct height

Benches are work tables used by fitters which must be steady and strong. Most benches are made of thick wood and are approximately 1 metre high. The top surface of the bench must be able to withstand shock because it may be subjected to sudden impact when work is being hammered or chiselled. Many benches have a vertical tool rack and a drawer underneath for storage of tools and workpieces.

A fitter's bench would normally have a vice fitted. The vice is used to hold the work steady when it is being shaped.

The vice must be securely fitted to the bench far enough forward to enable the work to extend below the top surface of the bench as shown. For maximum efficiency the vice's height should be the same as the fitter's elbow when he is working.

There are various designs of vices, most are cast iron and fitted with hardened steel jaws which may have a plain smooth surface or serrated grips. If the vice holding the workpiece has serrated jaws, a pair of inserts may be used to protect the work. These grips would normally be made from a soft material e.g. aluminium or fibre.

Standard serrated jaws

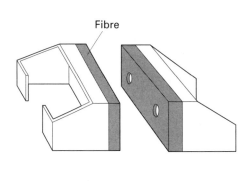

Fibre

Protective fibre grip inserts

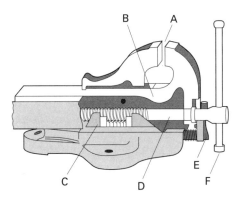

Cut-away view of a bench vice

A Hardened steel jaws
B Precision moving jaws
C Nut aligns body and jaw
D Steel screw and handle
E Quick release mechanism for opening jaw

Files and filing

A file is a hand tool used to remove material from workpieces. Various types of file are available, all are made from hardened and tempered high carbon steel. In the hands of a skilled fitter very small quantities of material can be removed to accurately finish a workpiece to its required shape and size.

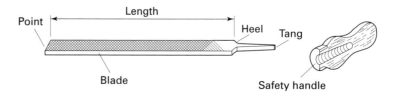

Names of parts of files

File handles

A file must *always* be fitted with a suitably sized handle fitted to the tang. This is for comfort and safety. *Never* use a file without a handle, as unprotected, the file's tang can seriously injure the palm of your hand. Files should never be used on a centre lathe.

Most file handles are wooden and have a metal ring around the front called a ferrule to stop the handle splitting. A split handle could cause splinters in your hand. Foreign matter embedded in a file's handle can also cut your hand – so always check the handle before starting work.

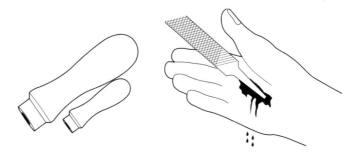

Wooden file handle with ferrule　　　Injury caused by using a file without a handle

Selection of file

Most fitters keep a range of files at their work area. Files are described by their **cut** of the teeth, **shape** of the section and **length** of the file.

The correct file for the job in hand should always be selected. The selection is determined by the material being filed and the shape of the finished workpiece. For example:

- A long file would normally be used for large workpieces, shorter files are for smaller, intricate work.
- A coarse file will remove material more quickly, smooth files are for finishing accurately to size.

1. File cuts

The pattern of the teeth on the file's body is the cut.

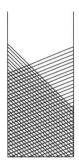

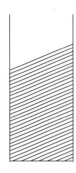

Single cut
For soft non-ferrous metals –
stays sharp longer as the teeth
are long edges, not points

Double cut
For most ferrous metals –
most popular file cut and is
widely available

Rasp
For roughing very soft
materials e.g. aluminium or
plastic – leaves a rough finish

2. Grade of file cut

Files are graded by the pitch (i.e. the spacing) of their teeth. The three most common grades and their uses are shown below. When gauging one file with another, the two files must be the same length, because the pitch of the teeth on the same grade of file varies with its length.

Bastard
Heavy metal removal – rough
finish

Second cut
General purpose – fair finish

Smooth
Fine finishing of work needing
a smooth surface finish

Note: Rough and dead smooth grades are less commonly available.

3. File shape
Common **file shapes**, and their uses are shown below.

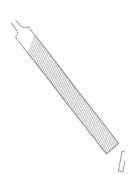

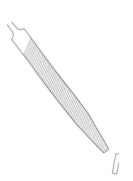

Hand
General filing – one edge has no teeth (safe edge) which prevents a shoulder from being filed or scratched

Flat
General purpose – being barrelled it can be used for filing surfaces precisely flat

Square
For rectangular holes, and slots with square corners

Ward
Filing inside narrow slots and grooves – narrower than most other files

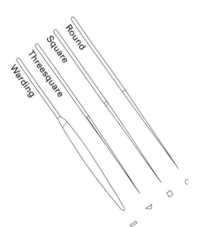

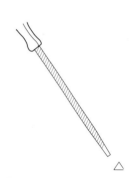

Swiss (needle) files
Miniature files used for finishing work and smaller workpieces. Large range of shapes are available: a few examples are shown here

Half round
Similar use as the flat file on front, curved side used for large internal curves

Round
For small internal curved surfaces and hole enlargement

Three square (triangular)
For finishing sharp corners and angles

4. Length of file
The length of a file is measured as the distance from the tip to the heel of the file (the length measurement of a needle file includes the handle).

A long file (approximately 12″ or 14″) would be selected for large work.
A short file (of say 4″ or 6″) would be selected for intricate work and accurate finishing.

Using files

When using a file, the workpiece is first secured in a suitable vice. If the workpiece is set at the correct height it will be much easier to file a surface flat.

- If the workpiece is set too high in the vice, the fitter will file upwards, causing the workpiece to be out of square.
- If the workpiece is set in the vice at the correct height, the fitter can file flat more easily, producing square workpieces.
- If the workpiece is set too low in the vice, the fitter will file downwards, causing the workpiece to be out of square.

The file is pushed over the work at an even and comfortable rate, applying downward pressure on the forward stroke and relieving the pressure on the return stroke. Use the full length of the file whenever possible. A number of different techniques are used by fitters as described below.

Straight filing

Straight filing involves gripping the file in one hand and using the other hand to guide the file lengthways across the work, the cutting pressure is applied with the palm of the hand. The feet are positioned for comfort and balance.

When finishing, apply pressure on the forward (away) stroke lightly with both hands as shown, and relieve the pressure on the return stroke as before.

Roughing – heavy pressure   Finishing – light pressure

Filing curves and radii is best done from the side of the vice, rocking the file as it is passed over the work. The surface should be compared to a radius gauge at regular intervals to check the material is being removed from only the correct places.

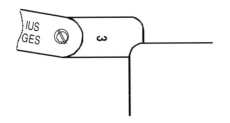
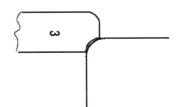
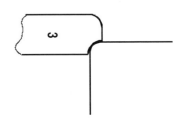

Correct: radius filed matches   Radius too large: too much   Radius too small: file more
radius gauge   metal has been removed   material off

Checking with a radius gauge

When filing curves and radii, stand in line with the vice jaws and swing the file as shown:

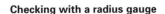

Start with elbow raised high   Mid-stroke   Finish stroke with hand low

Drawfiling a flat workpiece

Drawfiling

This is a technique used to finish surfaces to a high-quality surface finish. A surface finish of 0·8 μm can be achieved by drawfiling with a smooth file. Hold the file firmly at both ends, push and pull the width of the file along the length of the work.

Filing flat

To file an accurate flat surface takes much practice and patience.

First smear marking blue onto the top surface of a surface plate and rub the work on the 'blued' area. The marking blue will be transferred to the workpiece at the points of contact, known as high spots. The workpiece is then mounted in a vice and the high spots removed with a file. This process is repeated until the blue marks on the workpiece appear evenly spread over the surface being filed flat.

It is good practice to support the workpiece vertically with an angle plate while rubbing the workpiece on the surface plate. When finish-filing a broad surface flat, use a flat file because it is slightly barrelled in thickness, allowing the fitter to file parts of the surface without removing material from other areas.

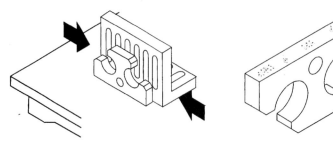

Rubbing the work on a surface plate   Note the high spots

Filing square

As the name suggests, filing square involves filing the edges of workpieces square to one another, often to form a datum for marking out.

Hold the work and a try square up to light and view the gap between the work and the try square's blade. Notice where the light passes through and where the workpiece makes contact with the try square's blade. Grip the workpiece in a vice and lightly file away the high spots (areas of contact) so the whole length of the try square's blade and stock are in contact with the workpiece.

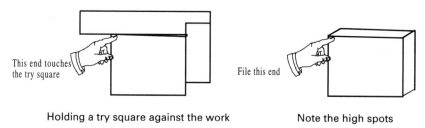

This end touches the try square

File this end

Holding a try square against the work   Note the high spots

Finishing

The trainee fitter must take care to only remove material from the areas necessary. This seems obvious but is, in practice, a difficult process. The marked lines should be constantly observed and not cut across until the component has been measured.

When finish-filing a surface's profile, check it frequently against a try square or surface plate and only remove small quantities of material from the high spots at a time.

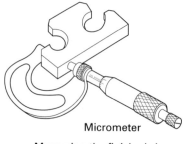

Micrometer

Measuring the finished size
with a micrometer

Care of files

- Store files separately, if files' teeth rub together they can become damaged. Many fitters hang their files in a rack.
- Keep files dry to stop them going rusty.
- Remove any clogged material from the teeth of files with a file card.
- When working on soft metals, apply chalk to the teeth of files to reduce the chances of clogging.
- Never hit anything with a file as the file could break.

Removing clogged material from a file with a file card

| Exercise 2.1 | *Drill drift* |

Mark out and make the drill drift using the procedure and tools indicated. Your finished work should be within the drawing limits.

On completion of the task, carefully measure your work and write in the table the actual sizes, noting any errors.

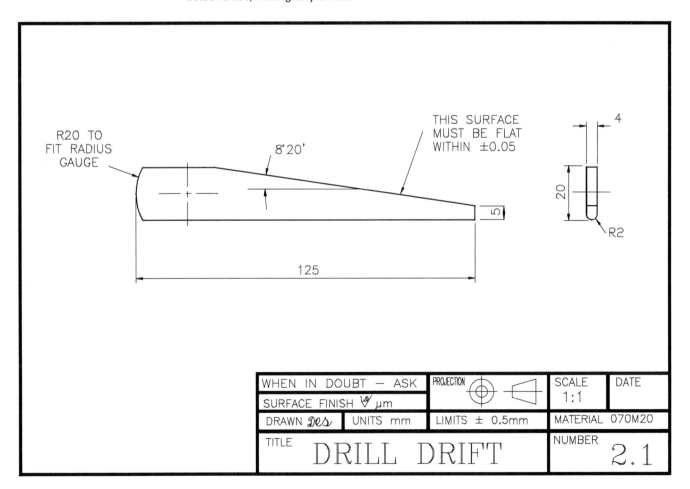

Planning

Procedure
1 Acquire material and check for size
2 Mark out all centre lines and edges
3 Dot punch profile
4 Check profile
5 Saw cut rough profile
6 File to just clear of marked lines
7 Finish file profile and check against drawing
8 Stamp name, de-burr and polish
9 Clean the work area

Tools and equipment selected
Marking out tools & equipment:
• metric 300 mm rule
• Odd leg caliper
• Scriber
• Dot punch
• $\frac{1}{2}$ lb hammer
Range of files
Radius gauges
Letter stamps

Complete the tables with the correct information.

Files used: state cut, shape, length	Reason for selection
1	
2	
3	
4	
Height of top of vice from floor	

Write here the checks made on files before using them to ensure they are safe and sharp.

1

2

3

Write here the hygiene procedures to be followed in the workshop.

1

2

3

Sketch

Make a dimensioned sketch of a hand file and a flat file showing clearly which type has a safe edge.

Hand file	Flat file

Finished inspection report

Component dimensions (mm)	Limits	Actual size	Error
1 Overall length 125 mm	125.5 124.5		
2 Overall height 20 mm	20.5 19.5		
3 Height 5 mm	4.5 5.5		
4 Radius 20 mm	To fit radius gauge		
5 Blade flatness	Feeler tight within 0.05 on blade length.		
Remarks			

Results

Is the workpiece to the drawing specification?　　　| Yes |　　　| No |

If the completed workpiece is below drawing specification, write here the reasons for any errors, stating clearly how the errors will be avoided in future.

Start date	End date	Time taken (hours)	Signed satisfactory by supervisor

Hacksaws

A hacksaw is a hand saw which is effectively used when large amounts of material, usually metals, are to be removed by cutting. However, before starting work a little time should be taken to choose a good quality hacksaw frame and select the most appropriate blade.

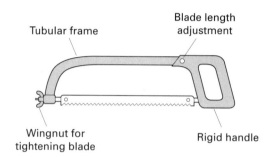

Hacksaw frame
The hacksaw frame shown above is adjustable to allow various blade lengths to be fitted, it has a comfortable handle and a rigid construction.

Selecting the hacksaw blade

Hacksaw blades are available in a range of **lengths**, **pitches** and **materials**.
The correct blade should always be selected. The selection is determined by the size, material and access to the workpiece being cut.

1. Length of hacksaw blade
The blade length is measured between the two small holes at the ends.
When selecting a blade for an adjustable hacksaw frame, choose a short blade if strength is important. However, a short blade would not be suitable for wide workpieces as the hacksaw frame would catch the workpiece.
Some hacksaw frames are not adjustable so you must use a standard length (300 mm) blade.

2. Pitch of hacksaw blade
The pitch is the teeth spacing, it is specified by the t.p.i. (teeth per inch). There are three pitches generally available: 18 t.p.i., 24 t.p.i. and 32 t.p.i.
Two general rules to follow when selecting the pitch of a hacksaw blade:

Rule A. Cut with as many teeth as possible without clogging the blade, so:

- Use **fine** pitch blades for **hard** metals (to get more teeth doing the work)
- Use **coarse** blades for **soft** metals (because there is space for the chips)

Rule B. Always keep three teeth in contact with the work at all times, so:

- Use **fine** pitch blades for **thin** sections (to maintain three teeth in contact with the workpiece)
- Use **coarse** pitch blades for **thick** metals (because there is space for the chips)

18 t.p.i.
Soft materials,
thick materials

24 t.p.i.
General purpose

32 t.p.i.
Hard materials,
thin materials including
thin wall tube

3. Hacksaw blade materials

Flexible Suitable for cutting mild steel and soft metals. Flexible blades made from high-carbon steel and are more durable so are used when access to the work is restricted and the blade may bend.

All hard Very hard high-speed steel but also quite brittle. 'All hard' blades are used when there is good access to the work and it is firmly secured in the vice.

Bi-metal High-speed steel cutting edges are welded onto a carbon steel backing, making them the most useful blade. Bi-metal blades are good for most applications as they are flexible and have hard teeth.

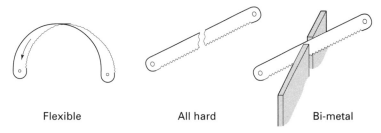

Flexible   All hard   Bi-metal

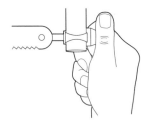

Hacksaw blade tensioning

Mounting the blade

The blade is mounted between the two pegs with its teeth facing away from the handle so that the cutting takes place on the forward stroke. The blade is tightened with the winged nut at the front of the frame. The blade should be taut and the frame not over stressed. Usually *three full turns* of the winged nut provide the correct tension to hold the blade.

Using hacksaws

When using a hacksaw it is important that the workpiece is first secured in a vice and the saw handle is held vertically with its frame in line with your arm. If you don't hold it properly, it becomes unsafe and blades may get broken, material may not be sawn straight and inaccurate sawcuts could be made.

Good and safe techniques are listed as follows:

- Wear safety glasses, if blade breaks, splinters could go anywhere.
- Select the correct blade.
- Check the blade for damage before starting work.
- Mount blade the right way round and apply tension.
- Take care to cut on the correct side of the line.
- Securely arrange the work in the vice so the sawcut is vertical.
- Cut near to the vice so the work will not vibrate.
- Stand with your arm and the saw's frame in a straight line.
- Stand so that you are feet are apart and you're steady.
- Work steadily with a stroke rate of approximately 40 strokes per min.
- Use the full length of the blade.
- The blade can be turned through 90 ° for sawing long pieces.

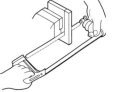

Usual method of holding a   Method of holding a hacksaw
hacksaw   for cutting extra long pieces

And remember: if the blade does get broken, it is best to finish the cut with a *worn blade*, a new one will jam in the previous slot and be at risk of breaking.

Junior hacksaw

The junior hacksaw is sometimes handy if a material must be cut which is inaccessible to full-sized hacksaw frames. A junior hacksaw has a frame which is often made from one piece of spring steel. The blades are usually the flexible type and have a fine pitch (32 t.p.i.).

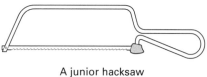

A junior hacksaw

Care of hacksaws

- Store hacksaws with the blade tension slackened.
- Keep hacksaws dry to stop them getting rusty.
- Hang the hacksaw in a rack.
- Protect the blade from being knocked.

Drilling on the bench drilling machine

Bench drilling machine

The bench drilling machine is a light machine used to drill small holes in workpieces when limited accuracy is required. Bench drilling machines are usually mounted on top of workshop benches.

A drill chuck with a capacity of approximately 13 mm ($\frac{1}{2}$") is usually mounted in the machine's spindle. The drill is secured in the chuck with a chuck key.

A small work table measuring approximately 300 mm square is clamped to the machine's pillar, its height is set and locked into position with a clamp.

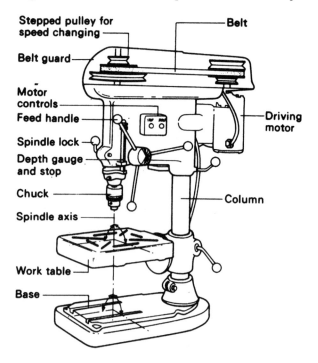

Bench drilling machine

The speed of the drill relates to the size of the drill and the metal being cut. If the drill rotates too fast, the drill could 'burn out' due to excessive friction; if it rotates too slowly then time would be wasted.

Usually five speeds are available. The speed is altered by manually changing the position of the belt so different sized pulleys are engaged.

Refer to Appendix IV. Look up the correct spindle speed for the size of drill/material type combination.

Setting the spindle speed

> **Safety** – *first isolate the machine by switching off the electrical supply.*

Set the spindle speed by removing the belt guard and manually changing the belt's position on the pulleys.

When changing a belt's position, start by moving it from a larger to a smaller diameter pulley.

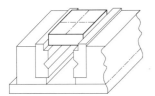

Workpiece held in a small machine vice

Work holding

The workpiece must be held securely while it is being drilled. The vice both grips and supports the work.

Workpieces are usually mounted in a small vice like the one shown.

Mount the workpiece and make sure the drill will 'break through' (i.e. when the drill begins to come out of the other side of the workpiece) without touching the vice.

Some small machine vices have a step on their jaws to support flat workpieces. There are also sometimes vees in the jaws to hold round materials either vertically or horizontally.

Make sure that there is space under the workpiece and the drill will not hit a vice jaw.

The vice's handle must be firmly held by the fitter to prevent it rotating during the drilling process. For large jobs the vice must be clamped firmly to the machine table.

Drilling the hole

The workpiece is positioned exactly underneath the drill point.

> **Safety** – *position the telescopic chuck guard around the cutting area and fix it into position before the spindle is turned on. The drill is manually fed through the workpiece with the large three-handled handwheel. Always feed slowly for the last bit while the drill is breaking through.*

The depth of the hole is displayed by viewing a calibrated rod on the front of the machine.

Particular care must be taken when the drill is 'breaking through'.

Measuring depth while drilling

> **Safety**
> *Never work on any machine until you have been shown how to operate it properly by a suitably qualified person.*

Your supervisor will arrange for you to be shown how to operate a bench drill. He will also explain the safety requirements, emergency stop procedure and introduce you to the following features:

- location of the workshop emergency stop buttons
- location of the bench drill's isolator switch
- drill chuck and chuck key
- spindle stop and start control
- how to change spindle speed
- the handwheel for feeding the drill
- work table and vice
- parallel bars for work setting
- various guards which must be used

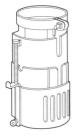

A telescopic drill guard

> *If you do not understand what you have been shown or if you are unsure how to proceed you must **ask!***

Exercise 2.2 *Slot cleaner*

Mark out and make the slot cleaner using the procedure and tools indicated. Complete the 'Tools and equipment selected' column. Your completed work should be within the drawing limits. Take special care with the two dimensions with fine limits.

On completion of the task, carefully measure your work and write in the table the actual sizes of your finished workpiece, noting any errors outside the permissible limits.

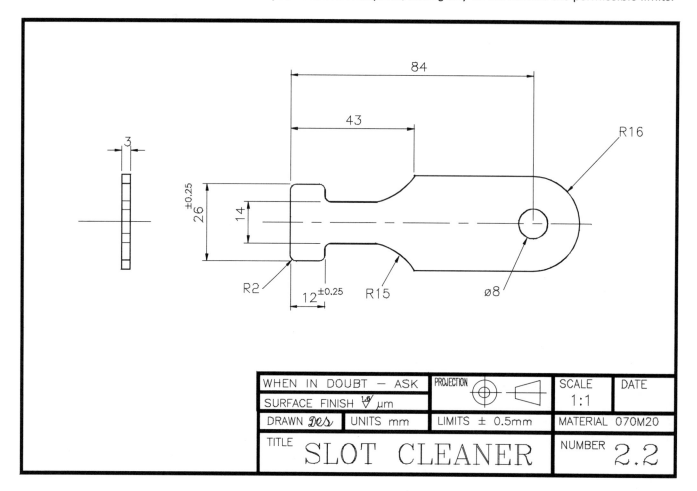

Planning

Procedure	Tools and equipment selected
1 Acquire material and check for size	
2 Mark out all lines, centre lines and edges	
3 Dot punch the profile and hole/radius centre	
4 Scribe the arcs with dividers	
5 Rough cut the profile with a hacksaw	
6 Finish file the profile	
7 Drill the hole	
8 Stamp name	
9 De-burr and polish	
10 Clean the work area	

Complete the tables with the correct information.

Saw blade type and pitch used	How checked before use		
Blade lengths accommodated in adjustable hacksaw frame	**Measurements**		
	Maximum	Nominal	Minimum
Drill spindle speed selected	**How selected**		

Write here the **safety procedures** to be observed while operating the bench drill.

1

2

3

Sketch

Make a sketch of the pulley arrangement on a bench drill showing the spindle speed for each belt position.

Finished inspection report

Component dimensions (mm)	Limits	Actual size	Error
26 length	26·25 25·75		
12 width	12·25 11·75		
Overall length 132	132·5 131·5		
14 radius	–		
2 radius	–		
Remarks			

Results

Is the workpiece to the drawing specification?

Yes	No

If the completed workpiece is below drawing specification, write here the reasons for any errors, stating clearly how the errors will be avoided in future.

Start date	End date	Time taken (hours)	Signed satisfactory by supervisor

Hole cutting tools

There are a wide range of cutting tools available for use in drilling machines. The cutting tools described below are used to prepare, rough out and finish holes accurately to size as well as cut special profiles. Always take care when handling hole-cutting tools as they have sharp edges and can cause nasty cuts and scratches.

Drills

1. Centre drills

Double-ended cutting tools are held in a drilling machine's chuck. They are used to produce accurately positioned small centre holes which guide the larger twist drills (described below).

Centre drills' points and stiff body make them unlikely to wander. Use a high speed to start the hole and drill to a depth of approximately half way down the 60° taper using *gentle* pressure.

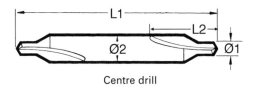

Centre drill

2. Twist drills

Available in a wide variety of sizes from approximately 0·4 mm (1/64") to 50mm (2"). They are used for cutting holes in workpieces. Most twist drills are made from high-speed steel (HSS). A drilled hole is quick to produce and can be used for a wide variety of functions, such as for fasteners to go through and for starting threads. Two types of twist drill are made as described below.

(a) **Parallel shank 'jobber' drills** (up to approximately ø13 mm). These drills have parallel shanks and are made out of HSS. They are held in a drill chuck and the size of the drill is normally engraved on the shank.

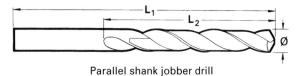

Parallel shank jobber drill

(b) **Morse taper shank drills** (from approximately ø10 mm to ø50 mm). The Morse taper shanks are used for accurate location and positive drive. The size of the morse taper depends on the size of the drill. There are eight sizes of morse tapers made, numbered 0 to 7. Size numbers 1, 2 and 3 are most common.

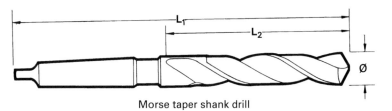

Morse taper shank drill

Reamers

Reamers are for accurately finishing pre-drilled holes to size and shape. They also produce a better quality surface finish than drilled holes. Reamers are supplied as hand or machine type. Both types having multiple cutting edges and are made from high-speed steel (HSS).

(a) **Hand reamers** – not used in drilling machines. These are hand tools used for enlarging pre-drilled holes accurately to size. Hand reamers are gripped in a tap wrench by the square on their shank. They are smeared with a special cutting fluid, held square to the workpiece, and steadily turned and manually pushed into the hole. Hand reamers are tapered for approximately one third of the length of their cutting edges end to assist alignment. This taper makes them unsuitable for finishing blind holes (holes that don't go right through the workpiece).

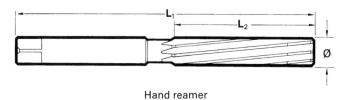

Hand reamer

(b) **Machine reamers** Held in a machine tool, this type of reamer has a chamfer on its leading edge because alignment is provided by the machine's construction. Most have a Morse taper shank. When setting a machine reamer in a drilling machine, the spindle speed should be set at half the speed for the equivalent size of drill and special cutting fluid applied.

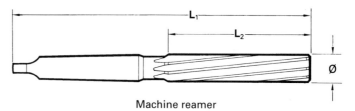

Machine reamer

Hole-forming tools

A hole forming tool is a cutting tool used to change the shape of a pre-drilled hole. This is usually required to enable the hole to accommodate a fastener (screw or rivet). Most hole forming tools are made from HSS and have either a straight or a morse tapered shank. Three of the most common types of hole forming tool are described below.

(a) **Countersink** – usually has a 90° included angle. This is used for flaring out the edge of holes for countersunk head screws or rivets.
   Also used for making a small countersink when riveting.
(b) **Counterbore** – used for making a recess so that cap head screws can fit flush when tightened. To use a counterbore, first drill a pilot hole to fit the counterbore's pilot, then follow by opening out the hole to the required depth with the counterbore.
(c) **Spotfacing tool** – used to clean up uneven surfaces around holes. A spotfacing tool is used when fasteners would otherwise tighten up against a rough surface.

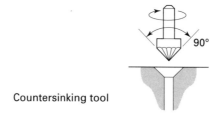

Countersinking tool

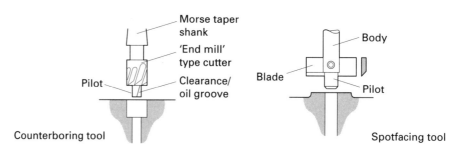

Counterboring tool

Spotfacing tool

Tool-holding devices used in drilling machines

All drilling machines are equipped with a device for securely holding the cutting tools. In nearly all cases this is either a drill chuck or a morse taper in the machine's spindle.

(a) **Drill chuck**. A drill chuck is a device used to hold parallel shank cutting tools in drilling machines. Most drill chucks have a capacity of approximately 13 mm ($\frac{1}{2}$") and are tightened with a special 'chuck key'. They are very quick to operate.

When using a drill chuck to hold a parallel shank drill, always make sure that there are no burrs on the sides of the drills shank or it will not run true.

Safety – always *remove the chuck key before starting the machine.*

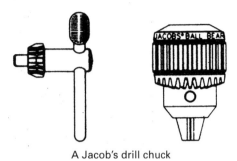

A Jacob's drill chuck

(b) **Morse tapers and sleeves** (sockets). Many machine tools are manufactured with a morse tapered hole in their spindle. The tapered hole is accurately machined to ensure the cutting tool rotates true. Morse tapers can transmit much more power than chucks and are generally used for larger drills and reams.

Cutting tools inserted into a morse taper will be held securely. If the morse taper of the cutting tool is not the same as that of the machine a morse taper sleeve must be used to make up the difference between the two tapers.

A drill drift is used to extract morse tapered tools from tapered spindles and sleeves. It fits into a slot in the spindle and is given a sharp tap with a hammer to eject the tool.

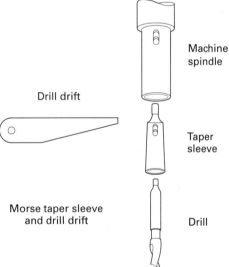

Drill drift

Machine spindle

Taper sleeve

Drill

Morse taper sleeve and drill drift

The pillar drilling machine

The pillar drill is a floor-mounted, free-standing drilling machine. Pillar drilling machines are used for drilling and reaming large holes accurately in position. They can also be fitted with special tools to allow then to tap (thread) holes. A machine centre or a centre finder can be fitted into the machine's spindle.

Features of the pillar drill

- Table equipped with 'tee slots' for clamping the work or workholding device into position
- Large range of spindle speeds
- Means of power feeding the drill through the work
- Morse taper in the spindle's nose which allows large hole cutting tools to be fitted directly into the spindle

- Gear drive train to spindle (not belts)
- Rigid and robust design
- Powerful electric motor
- Coolant supply to increase the life of the cutting tool and improve the work's surface finish

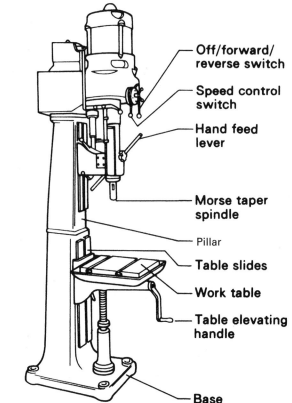

Off/forward/reverse switch

Speed control switch

Hand feed lever

Morse taper spindle

Pillar

Table slides

Work table

Table elevating handle

Base

Pillar drilling machine

Using a pillar drill

(a) Carefully mark out the centre of the hole. The hole's centre point is aligned with the spindle's centre line using a machine centre or a centre finder and the work secured in position.

Time spent lining up the work initially is well spent as the hole will be more accurately positioned

(b) Securely clamp the work in position. If it is to be held in a vice, the workpiece should be mounted on parallels, so that when the drill has passed through the work it does not damage the machine table.

(c) Raise the spindle, insert a drill chuck. Fit a centre drill into the chuck and set the spindle speed accordingly (see Appendix IV). Position the guard.

(d) Turn the spindle on and carefully feed the centre drill down into the work. It should be fed to a depth of approximately $\frac{2}{3}$ the depth of the 60° section of the centre drill.

(e) Keep the work clamped in the same position. Remove the centre drill from the chuck and fit a drill. Its position is exactly above the centre drilled hole so there is no lining up to do.

(f) The spindle speed must be reset, then the hole can be drilled with power feed and at the correct speed. (See Appendix IV for feed rates.)

(g) Substitute the drill for a larger one if it is outside the range of the chuck, a drill with a morse taper shank can be fitted directly into the spindle. Again it is necessary to re-set the spindle speed and guard.

(h) Feed the drill through the pre-drilled hole to open out the hole (increase its size).

(i) Should it be necessary, a machine reamer can be inserted into the spindle and the speed adjusted as appropriate. (Usually a speed of half the calculated speed for drilling is correct for reaming.) The reamer will accurately finish the hole to size and ensure it is exactly round.

Safety
Never work on any machine until you have been shown how to operate it properly by a suitably qualified person.

Your supervisor will arrange for you to be shown how to operate a pillar drill. He will also explain the safety requirements, emergency stop procedure and introduce you to the following features:

- location of the pillar drill's isolator switch
- drill chuck and chuck key
- spindle stop and start control
- how to change spindle speeds and feed
- the handwheel for feeding the drill and power feed engagement
- work table, vice and parallel bars for work setting

*If you do not understand what you have been shown or if you are unsure how to proceed you must **ask!***

Exercise 2.3   *Depth gauge body*

Mark out and make the depth gauge using the procedure indicated. Complete the tools and equipment selected column. Take special care with the two dimensions with limits, your finished work should be within the drawing limits.

On completion of the task, carefully measure your work and write in the table the actual sizes, noting any errors outside the permissible limits.

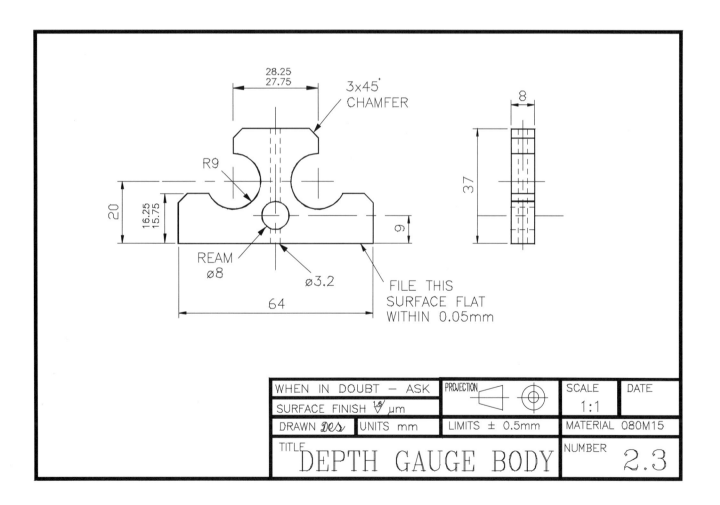

WHEN IN DOUBT – ASK	PROJECTION	SCALE	DATE
SURFACE FINISH ∇ μm		1:1	
DRAWN DAS	UNITS mm	LIMITS ± 0.5mm	MATERIAL 080M15
TITLE DEPTH GAUGE BODY		NUMBER 2.3	

Planning

Procedure	Tools and equipment selected
1 Acquire material and check for size 2 Mark out all lines, centre lines and edges 3 Centre drill, drill and chamfer each ⌀20 mm hole in turn 4 Carefully drill the ⌀3·2 mm hole starting at the top 5 Drill and ream the ⌀8 mm hole 6 Rough saw the profile 7 File base flat 8 File profile and chamfer as per drawing 9 Stamp name, de-burr and polish 10 Clean the work area	

Complete the tables with the correct information.

Saw blade pitch used	Reason for selection
Protective clothing needed while operating pillar drill	**Reason**
Drill spindle speeds selected	**How selected**

Write here about the following safety devices fitted to your pillar drill.

1 Emergency stop button

2 Cutting tool/chuck guard

3 Belt/pulley guard

Sketch

Make a sketch here to show how your workpieces were securely held whilst drilling the ⌀20 mm holes.

Finished inspection report

Component dimensions (mm)	Limits	Actual size	Error
16 mm shoulder	16.25 15.75		
Base flat	'Feeler tight' within 0.05 mm		
Overall length 64	64.5 63.5		
Chamfer 3×45	3.5 2.5		
Handle width	28.25 27.75		
Remarks			

Results

Is the workpiece to the drawing specification? | **Yes** | | **No** |

If the completed workpiece is below drawing specification, write here the reasons for any errors, stating clearly how the errors will be avoided in future.

Start date	End date	Time taken (hours)	Signed satisfactory by supervisor

Cutting internal screw threads

Internal threads are cut using thread cutting tools called 'taps'. Taps are precision cutting tools made from high-speed steel. The tap is screwed into a pre-drilled hole, as it goes into the hole its sharp cutting edges cut into the sides of the hole, cutting a thread profile.

Tapping can be carried out:

(a) by hand at a bench using a tap wrench to manually turn the tap. The process is described below.

(b) machine tapping (in a drilling machine, lathe or milling machine), using a 'tapping head'. This process is described later in this workbook.

Hand taps

Hand taps are supplied in sets of three. The name of the different taps are shown below together with their uses.

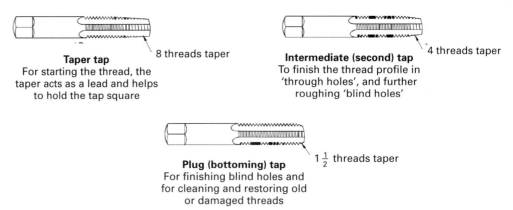

Taper tap
For starting the thread, the taper acts as a lead and helps to hold the tap square

8 threads taper

Intermediate (second) tap
To finish the thread profile in 'through holes', and further roughing 'blind holes'

4 threads taper

Plug (bottoming) tap
For finishing blind holes and for cleaning and restoring old or damaged threads

$1\frac{1}{2}$ threads taper

Tap wrenches

Tap wrenches are used to hold taps. The vee shape in the tap wrench's jaws grips the square at the end of the tap's shank. It is important to select a tap wrench which is a good fit on the tap or else the fitter can not control the tap properly.

A range of designs of tap wrench are available.

When selecting a tap wrench, the length of the wrench should be minimal to lessen the chances of tap breakage and increase 'feel'.

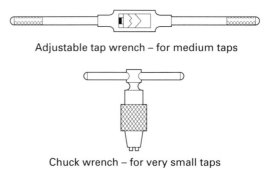

Adjustable tap wrench – for medium taps

Chuck wrench – for very small taps

Tap wrenches

Using hand taps to cut internal threads

The process of tapping is as follows:

(a) Find the *appropriate* size of hole to drill by referring to Appendix III. The thread's details may be given on an engineering drawing, or you may need to measure the screw.

If you are measuring a thread, use screw pitch gauges to assess the pitch, and a micrometer to find its diameter.

(b) Carefully mark out, centre punch and drill the hole to the tapping size.

(c) Select suitable size tap wrench to turn the tap (see tap wrenches).

(d) Smear some tapping compound onto each tap's surface before use. This compound helps the tap to cut by lubricating the cutting edges.

(e) Hold the work firmly in a vice.

(f) Mount the taper tap in the wrench.

(g) Place the tapered end of the tap into the hole.

(h) Hold the tap vertically and square to the hole's axis.

(i) Rotate the tap and press down at the same time.

(j) Once the tap starts to cut, turn it half a turn forwards, then relieve it a quarter turn backwards, advance again half a turn and relieve quarter turn, etc. until the thread

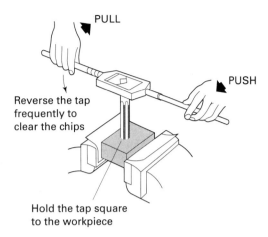

PULL

PUSH

Reverse the tap
frequently to
clear the chips

Hold the tap square
to the workpiece

Tapping in a vice

depth is achieved. (The relieving breaks up the chips so that the tap does not become jammed.)

(k) Remove the tap by unscrewing the tap wrench, and change the tap for the intermediate tap.

(l) Apply a little cutting compound and screw this tap into the hole to finish the thread form.

• Blind holes must be re-tapped with the plug tap to make sure the thread's full form extends to the bottom of the hole.

Care of taps

Always take care with taps, they are precision made and very brittle.

• If subjected to excessive force, taps will break. Broken pieces of taps are very difficult to remove from inside holes. A broken tap will probably scrap your workpiece.

• Always break up swarf by relieving the tap a quarter of a turn backwards for each half turn forwards.

• Always keep taps as a set: taper tap, intermediate tap and plug tap.

• Taps should be cleaned after use and stored in their box.

Cutting external screw threads

External threads are cut using tools called 'dies'. Dies are precision cutting tools made from high-speed steel. The die is screwed onto the end of a chamfered workpiece: as it goes onto the workpiece, its sharp cutting edges cut into the sides of the bar, forming a thread profile.

External screw thread cutting can be carried out:

• by hand, at a bench using a die stock to manually turn the die. The process is described below.

• by hand on a centre lathe using a die stock to manually turn the die. The process is described in the Turning section of this book.

• or on a centre lathe using a special die head. This process is also described later in this workbook.

Types of die used for hand thread cutting

The two main types of die are shown below together with their uses:

Circular split die
The most common type of die, it is used
for cutting external threads on bars.

Hexagon die nut
This type of die is screwed onto damaged or old
threads with a spanner to clean and restore its profile.

Die stocks

Die stocks are used to hold circular split dies. They have a bored recess which holds
the die.

Four common sizes of bore are: $\frac{13}{16}$"
1"
$1\frac{5}{16}$"
$1\frac{1}{2}$"

The size of die stock selected depends on the diameter of the die.
Die stocks have three small screws on their edge for adjusting the size of the die.

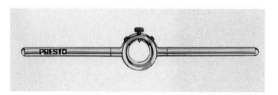

A die stock

When selecting a die stock, its length should be minimal to lessen the chances of
chipping the die and increase 'feel'.

Using dies to cut external threads

The process is as follows:

(a) Select the correct size material, its diameter must be the same as the outside
diameter of the finished thread.
(b) Chamfer the end of the workpiece with a file and mount it vertically in a vice.
(c) Select a suitable size die stock to mount the die.
(d) Insert the die into the stock. The two screws labelled A are slackened and screw B
is tightened to open the split die out to its maximum size.

90° lead

Chamfered workpiece

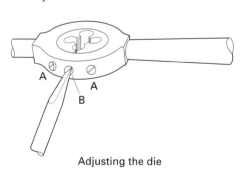

Adjusting the die

(e) Smear some tapping compound (cutting paste) onto the die's surface before use. This compound helps the die to cut by lubricating its cutting edges.

(f) Cut the thread:

- Hold the die stock square to the workpiece.
- Push firmly on the end of the die stock and turn it clockwise to screw it onto the workpiece.
- Check for squareness after the first two full turns.
- Turn the die stock $\frac{1}{4}$ turn back after each $\frac{1}{2}$ turn forwards to break up swarf. Continue until full length is reached.
- Remove the die by unscrewing it from the workpiece.

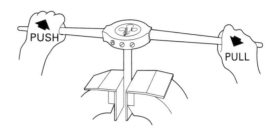

Cutting a thread with a stock and die on a vice

Check the thread

(a) Examine the surface.
(b) Compare it with screw pitch gauges.
(c) Try on a nut or thread gauge.
(d) If the nut is tight or will not go on:
    (i)   slacken screw B slightly
    (ii) tighten screws A
    (iii) apply a little more cutting compound
    (iv) screw the diestock onto the work again to finish its profile.

Care of dies

Always take care with dies, they are precision made and very brittle.

- If subjected to excessive force, dies will break.
- Always break up swarf by relieving the die a quarter of a turn backwards for each half turn forwards.
- Dies should be cleaned after use and stored in their case.

| **Exercise 2.4** | ## *Clutch tool handle* |

Make the clutch tool handle using the procedure and tools indicated. Complete the 'Tools and equipment selected' column. Take special care with the thread to ensure it is square to the axis of the body.

On completion of the task, carefully measure your work and write in the table the actual sizes of your finished workpiece, noting any errors outside the permissible limits.

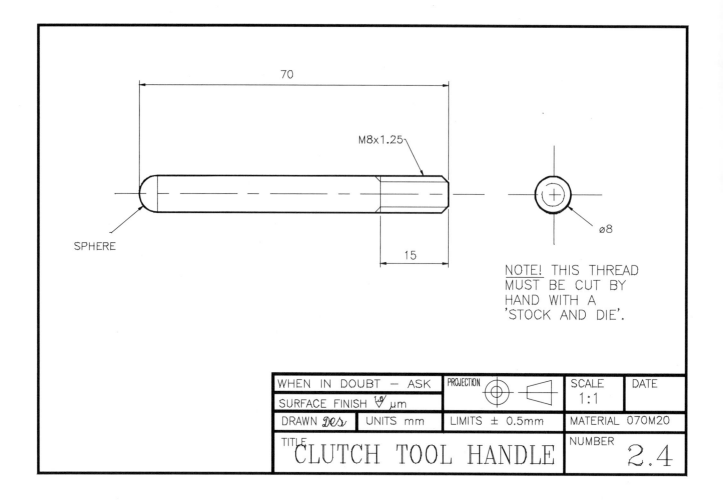

WHEN IN DOUBT — ASK	PROJECTION		SCALE 1:1	DATE
SURFACE FINISH ▽ μm				
DRAWN *Des*	UNITS mm	LIMITS ± 0.5mm	MATERIAL 070M20	
TITLE CLUTCH TOOL HANDLE			NUMBER 2.4	

Planning

Procedure	Tools and equipment selected
1 Acquire material and check for size	
2 File sphere on end and check with radius gauges	
3 Fit circular split die into a suitable diestock	
4 Adjust diestock to open out die to maximum size	
5 Cut thread	
6 Check thread with nut or thread gauge	
7 Check sizes	
8 Stamp name	
9 De-burr and polish	
10 Isolate machine and clean the work area	

Complete the tables with the correct information.

Size diestock used	How measured
Possible defects in external threads cut with a diestock	**Details of cause**
Method of checking thread	**How selected**

Write here the **safety procedures** to be observed to avoid dermatitis.

1

2

Sketch

Sketch a metric external screw thread profile showing clearly the thread's pitch, flank angle, major diameter and minor diameter.

Finished inspection report

Component dimensions (mm)	Limits	Actual size	Error
Overall length 70	70.5 69.5		
Thread length 15	15.5 14.5		
Sphere radius 4	ø4.5 ø3.5		

Results

Is the workpiece to the drawing specification?   Yes   No

If the completed workpiece is below drawing specification, write here the reasons for any errors, stating clearly how the errors will be avoided in future.

Start date	End date	Time taken (hours)	Signed satisfactory by supervisor

Shaping machine

Shapers, as they are commonly known, are simple machines to operate and quick to set up. They can be used to produce flat surfaces in a horizontal, a vertical or an angular plane on workpieces. The ram carries a cutting tool to and fro over the work, the cutting tool removes material from the work's surface as it traverses forwards over the work, hinging away from the work on the return stroke. For each cutting stroke, the work can be incrementally fed across the tool's path so the next stroke will remove more material. The stroke length and the feedrate can be adjusted to suit the workpiece's dimensions and the surface finish required.

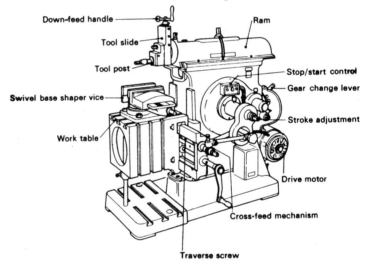

The shaping machine

Safety
Never work on any machine until you have been shown how to operate it properly by a suitably qualified person.

Your supervisor will show you how to operate the shaping machine, and will also explain the safety requirements, emergency stop procedure and introduce you to the following features:

- location of the isolator switch and start/stop lever
- how to set the stroke length, position and speed
- the handwheel for moving the cutting tool
- the method of feed engagement and setting feed rate
- work table, vice and machine guards

*If you do not understand what you have been shown or if you
are unsure how to proceed you must **ask!***

Exercise 2.5 *Toolmakers clamp*

Mark out and make the toolmakers clamp using the procedure and tools indicated, within the drawing limits. Complete the 'Tools and equipment selected' column.
   On completion of the task, carefully measure your work and write in the table the actual sizes, noting any errors.

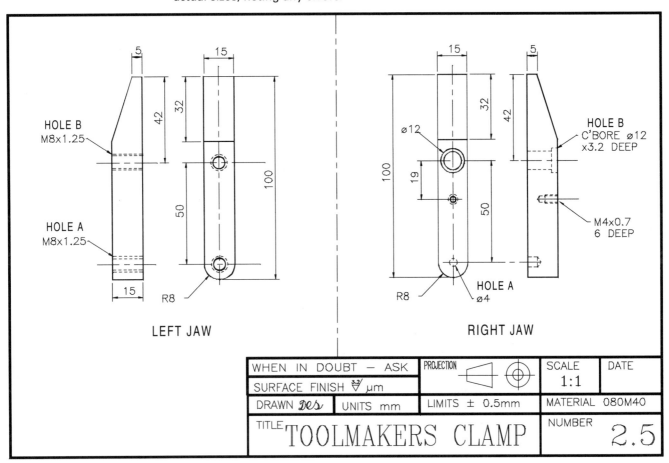

Planning

Procedure	Tools and equipment selected
1 Acquire material and check for size	
2 Mark out all lines, centre lines and edges on the left jaw	
3 Hold the two jaws together with toolmakers clamps	
4 Drill holes A through M8 × 1.25 hole at the tapping size	
5 Drill holes B through the left jaw and 5 mm deep into the right jaw with a ø5 mm drill	
6 Separate the parts	
7 Re-drill, counterbore and tap each jaw as appropriate	
8 Cut angular faces with shaper, file radius at ends	
9 Stamp name, de-burr and polish	
10 Clean the work area	

Complete the tables with the correct information.

Files used: cut, shape, length	Reason for selection
1	
2	
Selection of tools and equipment	
1 Thread size: (i) M4 × 0·7 (ii) M8 × 1·25	Drill size selected: (i) (ii)
2 Thread size (i) M4 × 0·7 (ii) M8 × 1·25	Length of tap wrenches used:
3 Name of tapping compound used	Where kept

Show your supervisor the features of a pillar drill listed below.

1 Power feed engagement lever

2 Two methods of holding cutting tools

3 Two methods of restraining workpieces whilst drilling

4 Method of guarding moving machine parts.

Sketch

Sketch your set up for drilling the two pairs of holes exactly in line.

Finished inspection report

Component dimensions (mm)	Limits	Actual size	Error
Hole centres	50.5 49.5		
Overall length	100.5 99.5		
c'bore depth	3.7 2.7		
Check thread form for excessive tearing	visual check		
Use appropriate gauges to check pitch of thread	Equipment used to check thread profile:		
Remarks			

Results

Is the workpiece to the drawing specification? | **Yes** | | **No** |

If the completed workpiece is below drawing specification, write here the reasons for any errors, stating clearly how the errors will be avoided in future.

Start date	End date	Time taken (hours)	Signed satisfactory by supervisor

Reaming

A reamer is a cutting tool used to *accurately* finish pre-drilled holes to size. Reamers have multiple cutting edges and are made from high-speed steel. They are designed to remove only *small* amounts of material and leave a *smooth surface finish* of approximately 0·8 μm, much better than an ordinary drill.

There are two types of reamer:

(a) Hand reamers
(b) Machine reamers

Reamers were introduced on pages 23–4 (hole cutting tools).

Hand reaming

(a) Accurately mark out and pre-drill the hole's position. The size of the hole is important – refer to Appendix V to select the correct drill size.

> *The size of a drilled hole is more likely to be accurate if it is first pilot drilled and then re-drilled to the required size.*

(b) Hold the work firmly in the vice with the hole's axis vertical.
(c) Apply a smear of tapping compound to the reamer's body.
(d) Hold the square on the reamer's shank in a tap wrench. The wrench should hold the reamer firmly.
(e) Hold the tap wrench in the palm of your hand and locate the end of the reamer in the hole. It will go into the hole part way as the first quarter of a hand reamer's length is tapered.
(f) Hold the reamer square to the hole's axis, rotate it clockwise and press it into the work at the same time.
(g) Remove the reamer from the hole by continuing to turn it clockwise.

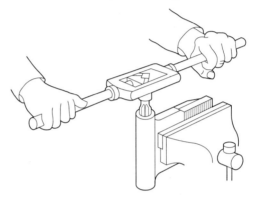

Hand reaming in a bench vice

Machine reaming

Generally, machine reamers are more accurate than hand reamers.

(a) Mark out the workpiece and clamp it accurately in position on a drilling machine's table.
(b) Centre drill and pre-drill the workpiece to the correct drill size after referring to Appendix V.
(c) Remove the drill and insert the machine reamer in the machine's spindle.
(d) Apply a little tapping compound to the reamer if coolant is not available on the drilling machine.

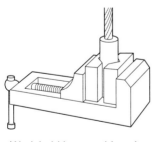

Work held in a machine vice ready for reaming

- If a morse taper shank reamer is used it might be necessary to use a morse taper sleeve. Remember that the machine holds the reamer straight and square to the workpiece.
- General practice is to use half the drilling speed and double the recommended feedrate for the equivalent drilled hole – refer to Appendix V (Reaming allowances).
- The machine holds the reamer square to the hole. Turn on the spindle and feed the reamer slowly through the hole. Machine reamers cut on the chamfered leading edge of their teeth. The sides of the reamer guide the body straight down the hole and prevent it from running out of true.
- Apply a generous supply of coolant, if it is available on the machine. If coolant is not available apply some tapping compound to the reamer's cutting edges.

(e) Withdraw the reamer with the drilling machine still running immediately after breaking through or reaching the required depth.

Exercise 2.6 *Drill stand*

Mark out and make the drill stand using the procedure indicated. List all tools used in the task. Your finished work should be within the drawing limits.

On completion of the task, carefully measure your work and record the actual sizes, noting any errors.

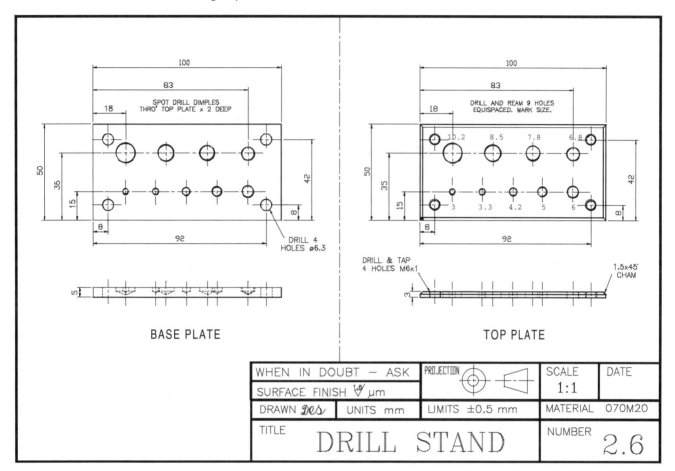

BASE PLATE

TOP PLATE

WHEN IN DOUBT — ASK	PROJECTION		SCALE 1:1	DATE
SURFACE FINISH ⩡ μm				
DRAWN *Des*	UNITS mm	LIMITS ±0.5 mm	MATERIAL 070M20	
TITLE DRILL STAND			NUMBER 2.6	

Planning

Procedure	Tools and equipment selected
1 Acquire material and check for size	
2 Mark out all lines, centre lines and edges	
3 Clamp both pieces together, drill M6 (tapping size) holes	
4 Tap four M6 × 1 holes in top plate	
5 Re-drill four base plate holes ø5·7 mm and ream ø6 mm	
6 Screw pieces together	
7 Mark out and drill 9 holes 5 mm deep	
8 File chamfer 1·5 × 45° round edge of top plate	
9 Stamp hole sizes in appropriate position	
10 Stamp name, de-burr, polish and clean the work area	

Complete the tables with the correct information.

The following holes are reamed. Write in the boxes the appropriate drill sizes required and the appropriate spindle speeds for reaming.

Ø3 mm	Ø5 mm	Ø6 mm
Size	Size	Size
Speed	Speed	Speed

Type of reamer used (hand or machine)	Reason for selection
Name of cutting tool used to machine countersink	How held in machine
Cutting fluids used (a) for tapping: (b) for reaming:	How applied to workpiece

Write here the **safety procedures** used while drilling.

1

2

3

Sketch
Make a clear sketch to illustrate how the depth is set on your drilling machine.

Finished inspection report

Component dimensions (mm)	Limits	Actual size	Error
Overall width			
Overall length			
Chamfer			
Corner hole positions			
Remarks			

Results

Is the workpiece to the drawing specification? | **Yes** | | **No** |

If the completed workpiece is below drawing specification, write here the reasons for any errors, stating clearly how the errors will be avoided in future.

Start date	End date	Time taken (hours)	Signed satisfactory by supervisor

Screwdrivers

Screwdrivers are designed to turn the heads of screwed fasteners. There are various designs and sizes of screwdriver blades and handles.

Selection of screwdrivers

1. Blades

The most important feature of a screwdriver is the point of its blade. When selecting a screwdriver, first look at the head of the screw, it should be one of these:

Straight	**Cross/Phillips**	**Pozi/Supadriv***	**Torx**
Standard slotted screwdriver tip – make sure tip fits the slot in both length and thickness	Fastener used in a wide variety of applications	Considered to be stronger than the cross head screw, notice the star	Used in the motor industry and for electronics components

*Pozi/Supadriv are registered trademarks of the European Industrial Services Ltd

When selecting a screwdriver, make sure the size and shape of its point match the shape of the screw's head and will be a good fit.

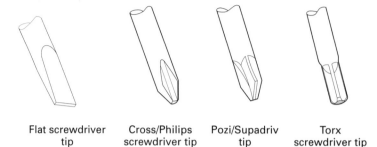

| Flat screwdriver tip | Cross/Philips screwdriver tip | Pozi/Supadriv tip | Torx screwdriver tip |

2. Handles

The shape and size of the handle affects the amount of 'turning effect' that can be applied to the screw head. A bigger handle is easier to turn than a thin one, and a handle with serrated grips is also easier to turn.

A screwdriver handle should be comfortable, different people prefer various styles for their own personal reasons.

For electrical work an insulated plastic handle *must* always be used. Some screwdrivers also have insulation along the length of the blade as well for further protection.

Never

- Hit a screwdriver with a hammer – it spoils the tip and can split the handle.
- Use a screwdriver to turn screws in a hand-held workpiece otherwise you could stab the palm of your hand with the screwdriver's blade.

Hexagon socket wrenches (allen keys)

Hexagon socket wrenches are used for turning hexagon socket head screws (known as cap screws) and other special screws. The size of the allen key is its measurement across the flats of the hexagon (A/F).

Made of high-quality tool steel, allen keys look like bent pieces of hexagonal bar, a screwdriver type is also available.

The allen key is inserted into the socket head screw and turned, thus tightening or undoing the fastener. It is important to use the correct size of allen key. It should fit firmly in the socket head screw with no wavering.

Hexagon socket wrench (allen key)

| Grub screw | Counter-sunk head screw | Cap screw |

Types of socket head screw

Spanners

Spanners are used for tightening and loosening hexagonal and square head nuts and bolts. All good spanners are made of high-quality alloy steel containing chromium and vanadium to increase their strength and toughness.

Most spanner manufacturers supply spanners in a range of metric (mm), English (BSW & BSF) and American (A/F) sizes. Spanners are available in a range of styles to suit almost every job.

Open ended
Angled head of spanner allows access to nuts near obstructions.

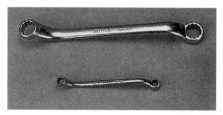

Ring
Grips nut all way round. High strength, can not be used on pipes. Ends are different sizes.

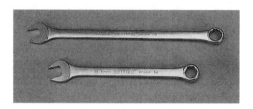

Combination
One end a ring, other open ended. Both ends fit same size nut. Provide versatility.

Adjustable
Grips and turns almost any size of nut. Can be clumsy. Use when correct size spanner is not available.

C-spanner

C-spanners are special spanners used for loosening and tightening round slotted nuts.

Round slotted nuts are thin in section and evenly balanced. This type of nut is frequently used to hold grinding wheels in position.

The C-spanner is hooked into a notch on the edge of the nut and it is turned by the long handle.

C-spanner

Nut requiring a C-spanner

Engineer's socket sets

Socket sets are made up with a variety of wrenches, extension pieces and sockets to fit a range of size nuts. They are strong and versatile. A large range of accessories enable fasteners to be tightened in positions when the end of the nut is accessible.

Sockets can not be used on nuts where access to the end of nut is restricted, either because it is close to something or it is on a pipe.

Torque wrenches

If nuts are tightened too tight the shank of a nut or bolt can be permanently stretched and weakened. For many applications it is important to tighten the bolt as tight as possible without causing any weakening.

The maximum tightness allowed depends on a number of factors, principally the material and size of the stud/shank. The tightness of a bolt is measured in units of torque called newton/metres. A torque wrench measures the amount of torque being applied to a bolt. Most torque wrenches use sockets and are set by turning a screw on the handle to set the required torque. When the correct torque is applied, the torque wrench 'clicks'.

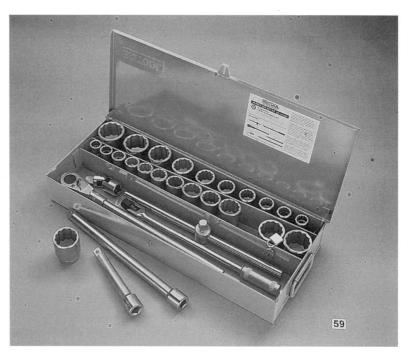

A good-quality socket set

Using a torque wrench

Most bolts tightened to specified torque settings are made out of a special high tensile steel. There are a number of quality grades of bolts; these grades indicate the strength of the bolt – 8·8 is a fairly popular quality grade of metric bolt. If the manufacturer's data is not available you can find the correct torque for a metric coarse bolt by referring to Appendix VI which lists some common torque wrench settings.

To set the torque wrench turn the adjusting screw on the end of the handle so that the correct torque is shown on the gauge. The socket is put onto the wrench and attached to the bolt. Turn the wrench by the handle and when the correct torque is reached there is a click and the wrench 'gives'. The bolt is now tightened to the correct torque.

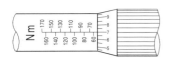

Torque wrench set at 57 N/m

Using a torque wrench

Selection and use of spanners and wrenches:

* Always take care to select a well-fitting spanner or wrench.
* Check for damage or wear before use.
* Select a tool which is most comfortable to use.

- Pull tools towards you (instead of pushing) in case you slip.
- Wipe away any oil from tools before storing.

Never:

- Extend spanners or wrenches with a pipe to increase leverage.
- Tilt open-ended spanners at an angle to the screw head, it is likely to slip.
- Hammer on a spanner or wrench.
- File or grind a spanner to make it fit.

Pliers

Pliers are hand tools for gripping irregular-shaped workpieces. Pliers are made of high-carbon tool steel and often have insulated handles. They are available in a range of designs and sizes, the most popular of which are shown and described below.

Selection of pliers

When selecting pliers it is necessary to be aware of the styles available and their applications. Consider the drawings and uses listed below.

The size of plies refers to the overall length including the jaws and handles; those with longer handles provide more leverage and a tighter grip of the workpiece.

Flat nose
Used only for gripping thin objects.
The short flat jaws are serrated inside
and hardened.

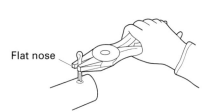

Combination
Jaws incorporate serrated flat grips,
splined pipe grips and two types
of wire cutters.

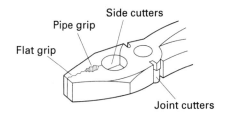

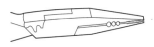

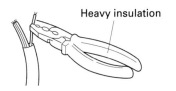

Snipe nose
Snipe nose jaws help with handling
small objects and give a better
view of work.

Electricans
Insulation on handles withstands high
voltages; used as combination pliers.

Using pliers

- Hold the workpiece in the jaws as close to the hinge as possible to get the tightest grip.
- Hold pliers at the end of the handles to get maximum grip.
- When working with high-voltage electrical appliances, always ensure the insulation is intact on the handles.
- Do not use pliers for gripping nuts instead of spanners – the pliers could spoil the nut's hexagonal shape.
- When cutting with the pincer blades always make sure your hand won't get trapped between the handles if the workpiece suddenly breaks.

Pipe wrench (stillson)

Pipe wrenches are for turning pipes. The serrated jaws of the pipe wrench can be adjusted to fit over a pipe.

As you pull on the pipe wrench's handle, the jaws grip the pipe, turning it.

Pipe wrenches do damage the surface of workpieces but this is not generally a problem with pipework systems.

Safety – *you must not extend the handle of a pipe wrench to increase leverage.*

Exercise 2.7 — *Gate valve*

Prepare a clean and tidy work area and plan a dismantling sequence for the gate valve, (Your supervisor may give you another suitable assembly to dismantle for this exercise.) Your dismantled work should be carefully examined and cleaned. Report any defects which would cause the components to fail.

Ask your supervisor to verify your report and confirm the workpiece was dismantled correctly. Re-assemble the gate valve and check to make sure that it opens and closes correctly. The main screws on the body should be tightened to 75 N/m with a torque wrench.

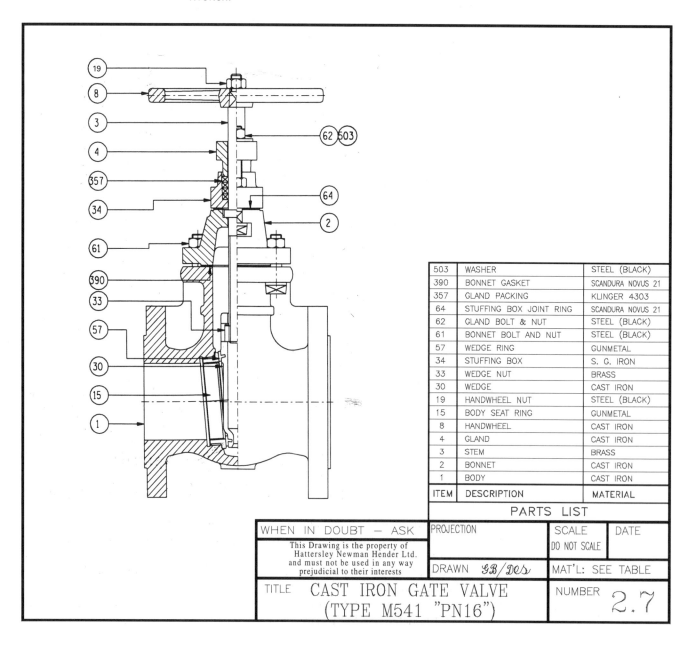

ITEM	DESCRIPTION	MATERIAL
503	WASHER	STEEL (BLACK)
390	BONNET GASKET	SCANDURA NOVUS 21
357	GLAND PACKING	KLINGER 4303
64	STUFFING BOX JOINT RING	SCANDURA NOVUS 21
62	GLAND BOLT & NUT	STEEL (BLACK)
61	BONNET BOLT AND NUT	STEEL (BLACK)
57	WEDGE RING	GUNMETAL
34	STUFFING BOX	S. G. IRON
33	WEDGE NUT	BRASS
30	WEDGE	CAST IRON
19	HANDWHEEL NUT	STEEL (BLACK)
15	BODY SEAT RING	GUNMETAL
8	HANDWHEEL	CAST IRON
4	GLAND	CAST IRON
3	STEM	BRASS
2	BONNET	CAST IRON
1	BODY	CAST IRON

PARTS LIST

WHEN IN DOUBT — ASK

This Drawing is the property of Hattersley Newman Hender Ltd. and must not be used in any way prejudicial to their interests

PROJECTION

SCALE DO NOT SCALE

DATE

DRAWN *GB/DCS*

MAT'L: SEE TABLE

TITLE CAST IRON GATE VALVE (TYPE M541 "PN16")

NUMBER 2.7

Planning 1 – dismantling

Procedure	Tools and equipment selected
1 Acquire gate valve from store	
2	
3	
4	
5	
6	
7	
8	
9	
10 Clean the work area	

Remove two different sized screws from the gate valve and assess their:
- size (e.g. $\frac{7}{16}$")
- thread form (e.g. Whitworth)
- pitch (e.g. 14 t.p.i.)

	Size	Thread form	Pitch
Screw thread 1			
Screw thread 2			

Planning 2 – assembly

Planned re-assembly procedure	Tools and equipment selected
1 Acquire gate valve components from store	
2	
3	
4	
5	
6	
7	
8	
9	
10 Clean the work area	

Complete the tables with the correct information.

Tools used
1 Types of pliers used:
2 Types and sizes of spanners used:
3 Type of screwdrivers used:
4 Types of wrenches used:

Notes on methods used to dismantle any particulary difficult fasteners.

1

2

Write here the reasons why the work area must be kept clean and tidy.

Write here the safety checks made on all hand tools before use.

1

2

3

Sketch

Sketch a detailed drawing of a thread gauges measuring a screw's pitch.

Does the gate valve work as it should?	**Yes**	**No**

If the completed workpiece does not work as it should, write here the reasons for any defects, stating clearly how they could be rectified.

Start date	End date	Time taken (hours)	Signed satisfactory by supervisor

Hammers

Hammers are important tools and must be used correctly and safely. Their main uses are:

- Tapping marking tools
- Riveting
- Chiselling
- Driving things into position

Hammers are identified by their shape and weight, some types of hammer are shown here.

Ball pein	**Cross pein**	**Straight pein**	**Soft faced**
Face of hammer for general purpose; ball pein for spreading work when riveting	Pein for riveting in awkward corners; front face used for general work; supplied in lighter weights		Plugs made of raw hide, aluminium or copper; used when the component being hit must not be damaged.

Most hammers are available in a range of weights, typically between 225 gm ($\frac{1}{2}$ lb) and 900 gm (2 lb). Bigger hammers than this are called sledge hammers and are used for very heavy work.

Hammer handles are made from good quality ash or hickory wood.

Safety
Always hold a hammer firmly at the end, as shown.

Correct method of holding a hammer

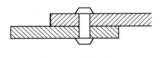

Round head rivet

Before using any hammer always carry out the following safety checks:

- Head is tight on the shaft.
- Shaft is not split.
- Head is not cracked or mushroomed.
- The handle is dry and not slippery.

Pan head rivet

Riveting

Riveting is the process of beating out the end of a special pin (called a rivet) or screw to produce a fastening that will not work loose if it is subjected to vibrations.

To form a flush (smooth) rivet, there must be some space for the excess material to fill when it is deformed. Usually a countersink is made in the workpiece for the deformed part of the rivet to fill. The rivet is then inserted into the hole and beaten with the ball pein of a hammer until its end is deformed and fills the countersink.

To finish the surface smooth, it must be carefully filed flat with a smooth file.

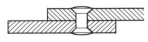

A countersunk riveted joint filed smooth

Exercise 2.8	*Assembling the drill stand*

On completion of Exercises 2.6 (drill stand plates) and 3.3 (drill stand legs), plan a detailed assembly procedure. Assemble the components by riveting the screw threads into the countersunk holes in the top plate. Remember, the legs must be screwed in tightly.

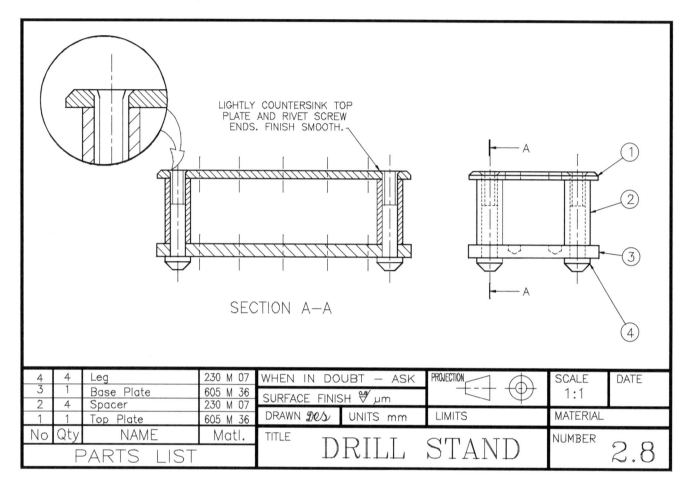

LIGHTLY COUNTERSINK TOP PLATE AND RIVET SCREW ENDS. FINISH SMOOTH.

SECTION A–A

4	4	Leg	230 M 07
3	1	Base Plate	605 M 36
2	4	Spacer	230 M 07
1	1	Top Plate	605 M 36
No	Qty	NAME	Matl.
		PARTS LIST	

WHEN IN DOUBT — ASK

SURFACE FINISH ∇ µm

DRAWN *DES*   UNITS mm

PROJECTION

LIMITS

SCALE 1:1   DATE

MATERIAL

TITLE **DRILL STAND**

NUMBER **2.8**

Planning

Procedure
1 Acquire components and finally check for size
2
3
4
5
6
7
8
9 De-burr and polish
10 Clean the work area

Tools and equipment selected

Complete the tables with the correct information.

Tool used to tighten legs	Reason for selection

Hammer used for riveting (shape, material and weight)	Reason for selection

List safety checks carried out on hammer(s) before starting to rivet the screw ends.

1

2

3

Sketch

Sketch a detailed drawing of the tools used to assess the surface texture which is specified as 1·6 μm.

Results

Is the workpiece to the drawing specification?   Yes   No

If the completed workpiece is below drawing specification, write here the reasons for any errors, stating clearly how the errors will be avoided in future.

Start date	End date	Time taken (hours)	Signed satisfactory by supervisor

Cold chisels

Cold chisels are commonly called chisels. Chisels are used with hammers for removing large amounts of material by hand. A variety of shapes are available, each having its own particular application.

Types of chisel

Flat
Used for splitting nuts, cutting sheet metal in a vice and general material removal

Cross cut
Used for cutting fine slots e.g. keyways

Diamond nose
Access to and sharpening of internal corners

Round nose
Used for cutting rounded grooves for oilways in machine tool slideways

Using chisels

(a) Wear safety glasses and erect screens to protect colleagues from flying chips.
(b) Hold the chisel in the middle of its shank with a gloved hand for safety.
(c) The chisel will need to be inclined at approximately 25°–30° depending on its point angle (60° for general use) and the material you are cutting.
(d) Strike the chisel firmly and repeatedly with a hammer.

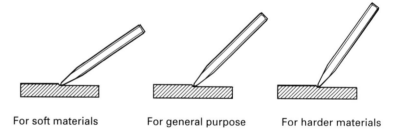

For soft materials   For general purpose   For harder materials

Dangerous
Mushroomed head

Safe
Correctly ground

Safety – always:

- Wear safety glasses and a glove when chiselling.
- Use a screen to protect others from your flying chips.
- Hold the hammer properly.

Safety – never:

- Use a chisel with a mushroomed head. (Pieces of 'mushroom' can fly off causing injury.)

Grinding chisel points

The point angle of chisels depends on the material to be cut. Generally chisels are sharpened to an angle of 60°. For softer materials slightly more acute (sharper) point angles are appropriate as the chisel would cut more quickly. For harder materials, a slightly more obtuse (blunter) point angles would be used as it makes the edge last longer.

Correct chisel point angles for common materials:

Aluminium	Brass	Bronze	Cast iron	Mild steel	High carbon steel	Hard alloy steel
30°	50°	60°	60°	55°	65°	65°

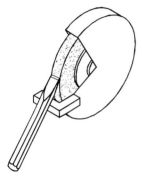

Sharpening a chisel

When sharpening a pointed instrument (e.g. a punch, scriber or a chisel), hold it vertically against the grinding wheel at the appropriate angle.

Press the instrument lightly against the revolving grinding wheel; the grinding marks will lie away from the edge. This will help to reduce friction in the cutting process and lengthen the edge life of the tool.

Take care not to overheat the point while sharpening it; keep a supply of cooling liquid nearby e.g. water or coolant from a machine tool.

You can tell if the tool point is too hot as it will turn blue. If this happens it will need re-hardening and tempering.

Safety – *while sharpening a chisel, turn it round and remove any mushrooming from the chisel's head. Mushrooming is dangerous as pieces fly off and can hit you.*

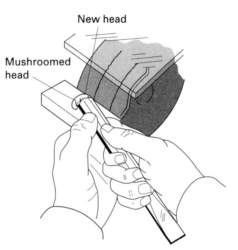

Removing 'mushrooming' from a chisel's shank

Ask your supervisor to show you how to use a grinding machine to grind a chisel's point. Notice the positions of the machine guards and rests.

Safety – always:

- Wear safety glasses.
- Wear appropriate protective clothing.
- Use the machine screens provided.
- Make sure the gap between the wheel and rest is minimal.

Safety – never:

- Work on a grinding machine of any description without being shown how to operate it.
- Touch a grinding wheel when its going.
- Try to stop a grinding wheel with anything.

| **Exercise 2.9** | *Sharpening chisels* |

Using a safe procedure, sharpen the following tools:

(a) Dot or centre punch
(b) Scriber
(c) Flat chisel

Use a protractor or point angle gauge to assess the angle of the tools after grinding. Your finished tools should have the correct lay patterns (grinding marks) and correct angles.

On completion of the task, carefully measure your tools' angles and complete the tables below.

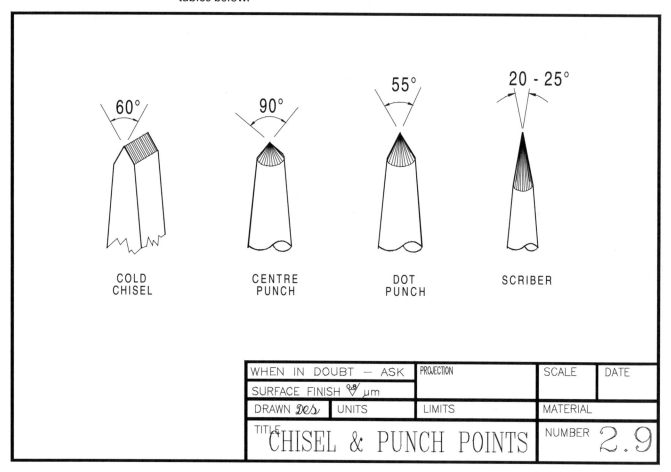

Complete the tables with the correct information.

Safety equipment used	Function of safety equipment
1	
2	
3	

Write here two checks for chisels before use to ensure they are safe.

1

2

Component dimension	Angle	Actual angle	Error
Scriber	20° to 25°		
Dot punch	60°		
Centre punch	90°		
Chisel	60°, or other... (depending on metal)		

Name the coolant used while grinding the instruments.

Sketch

Sketch a detailed drawing of:

Safety screens correctly adjusted for the off-hand grinding machine.	Machine work rest correctly adjusted for the off-hand grinding machine.

Test your newly sharpened tool and examine the point after checking.

1 Does it work properly?

2 Is the point still sharp?

List the safety precautions relevant to using grinding machines regarding screens.

1

2

Names of relevant laws specific to:

1 Grinding machines

2 Abrasive wheels

Start date	End date	Time taken (hours)	Signed satisfactory by supervisor

| **Exercise 2.10** | *Basic bench fitting test* |

The multiple choice question paper will only be issued to candidates by their supervisor on satisfactory completion of the appropriate exercises. The answer sheet below must be completed by the candidate when the questions are issued.

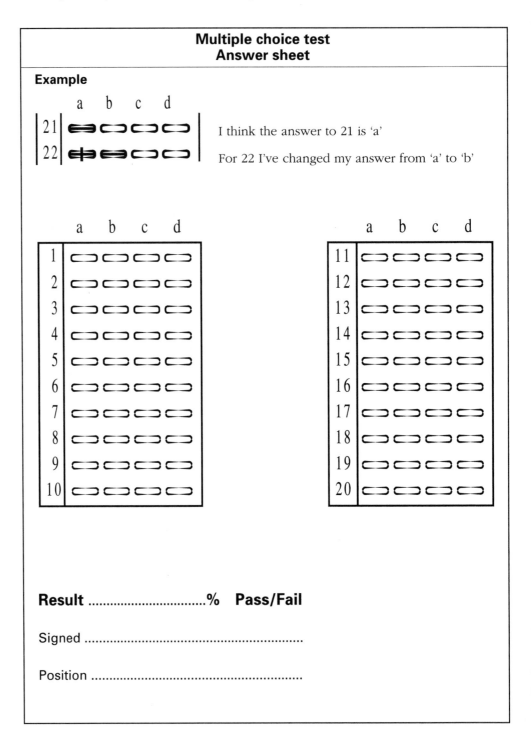

Chapter 3

Basic centre lathe turning

Exercise		Page	Date	Signed by Trainer
3.1	Turning exercise	69		
3.2	Clamp studs	73		
3.3	Drill stand legs	79		
3.4	Clutch tool body	87		
3.5	Boring exercise	94		
3.6	Depth gauge parts	101		
3.7	Toolmakers clamp screws	105		
3.8	Multi-choice test on all work in this chapter	108		
The trainee always observes personal protection/hygiene procedures				
The trainee has been observed to wear appropriate protective clothing				
The trainee has been observed to keep the work area clean and tidy				
The trainee has been seen to observe Health & Safety requirements and observes good working practices				

The centre lathe

The machine shown below is a centre lathe. Centre lathes are versatile machines operated by a machine operator called a turner.

Centre lathes are used to turn cylindrical workpieces, the profiles of which include:

- parallel diameters
- tapered diameters
- drilled or reamed holes
- accurately bored holes
- externally threaded diameters
- internally threaded holes

The work is held in a work-holding device and rotated. Cutting tools are secured in the machine's tool post and traversed along or across the workpiece's axis, thus removing material and producing the cylindrical shape.

Typical turned components are:

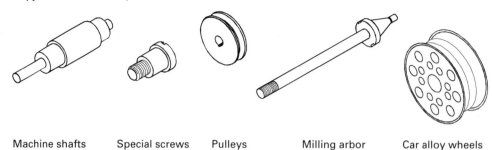

Machine shafts   Special screws   Pulleys   Milling arbor   Car alloy wheels

The fundamental parts of a centre lathe are labelled on the diagram below.

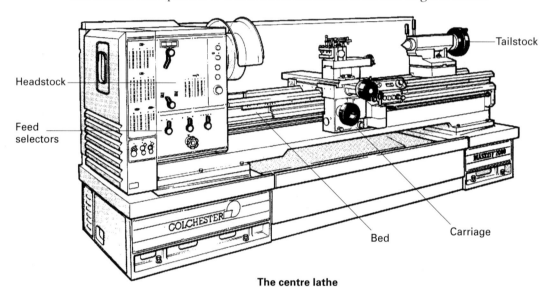

The centre lathe

1. **Headstock**

The large cast iron housing on the left-hand side of a centre lathe. The headstock houses the machine's spindle and two gear boxes.

The gear boxes enable the spindle's speed to be selected and the speed of the cutting tool movement to be adjusted i.e. the feed rate. The headstock has various levers to set the speeds and feed rates.

2. **Spindle**

Protruding from the headstock is the spindle's nose onto which various work-holding devices can be attached. There are various methods of fixing the work-holding device (see page 82) to the spindle. Two common types are illustrated below.

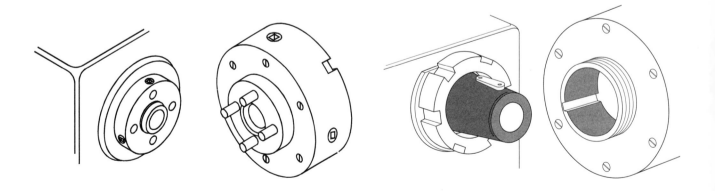

Cam lock (D fitting) spindle nose and chuck   Taper and nut (L fitting) spindle nose and chuck

3. Bed

Made of cast iron, the lathe bed is the machine's main slideways. Its top faces are accurately machined with flats and vee shaped slides to provide location for the machine's carriage and tailstock. The carriage traverses along the outer slideways while the tailstock runs along the inner slideways.

To resist twisting, the bed must be rigid and is therefore braced with ribs.

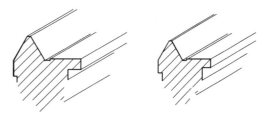

Section through a centre lathe's bed

4. Carriage

The centre lathe carriage can be traversed along the bed, either manually or automatically, carrying the cutting tool, the cross slide and the compound slide.

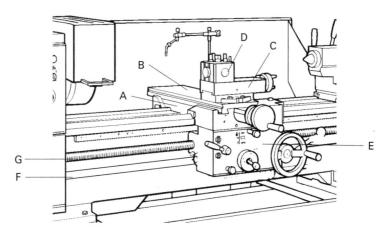

Detail of lathe carriage

The carriage is an assembly of the following components:

A *The saddle*	Traverses along the bed's slideways. On top of the saddle are the cross slide, compound slide and the tool post. Usually there is a nut on top of the saddle to enable it to be locked into position.
B *The cross slide*	Slides at 90° to the spindle's axis. The cross slide is operated by a graduated hand wheel feeding the cutting tool forwards to remove material from the workpiece. Cross slides can be moved automatically under 'power feed' while facing the end of a bar.
C *The compound slide*	Can be set at any angle to allow the cutting tool to be fed at an angle to the workpiece, producing a taper. The compound slide is operated by a small hand wheel.
D *The tool post*	Which houses the cutting tool.
E *The apron*	The front part of the carriage assembly. It houses various control levers and hand wheels. The apron is connected to the machine's gear box via the feed shaft (**F**) and the lead screw (**G**).

5. Tailstock

The tailstock is used for mounting various hole cutting tools (e.g. drills and reamers) or a machine centre (to support a long workpiece).

It is mounted on the bed's inner slideway and can be manually positioned. It can be locked into any position on the bed with a lever.

The tailstock contains a barrel which can be wound forward and backwards by a handwheel. The barrel can be locked in position with a second lever. There is a morse tapered hole in the tailstock barrel which is used to hold hole cutting tools and machine centres.

When measured from the bed, the height of the point of a machine centre mounted in the tailstock barrel is exactly the same as the height of the point of a machine centre mounted in the spindle.

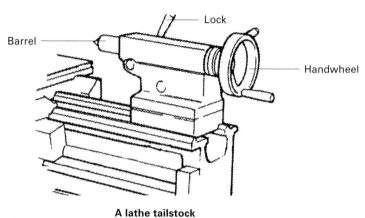

A lathe tailstock

6. Centre lathe sizes

The size of a centre lathe is measured in two ways:

(a) The centre distance – the maximum distance between the tailstock and headstock centres

(b) The centre height – the maximum work radius which can be held

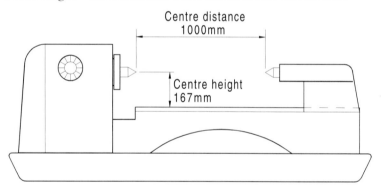

Lathe measurements
Centre lathe shown is 1000 mm 'between centres' and 167 mm 'centre height'.

Eight basic techniques used to produce turned components on a centre lathe are shown below.

1. Turned parallel diameters	2. End-faced square	3. Tapered diameter	4. Drilled or reamed hole
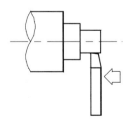	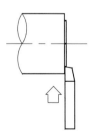	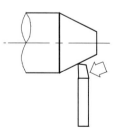	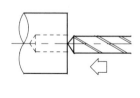
Cutting tool fed parallel to workpiece's axis.	Cutting tool fed across workpiece's axis.	Cutting tool fed at an angle to workpiece's axis.	Hole cutting tool fed along workpiece's axis.

| **5. Knurled thumb grip** | **6. Bored hole** | **7. External and internal threads** | **8. Grooved and Parted-off workpiece.** |

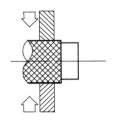 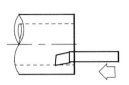 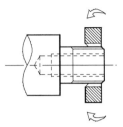 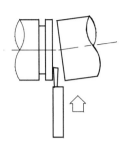

| Knurling tool impresses pattern into workpiece's surface | Boring tool fed into end of workpiece | Taps and dies used by hand or with power | Parting-off tool fed directly into workpiece's surface |

Mounting the work in a three-jaw self-centring chuck

Chucks are a quick and convenient method of work-holding. Lathe chucks are mounted on the end of the spindle (the spindle nose). There are three main types of lathe chuck in common use:

- Three-jaw self-centring chuck
- Four-jaw independent chuck
- Spring collets

All are described on pages 82–3, together with other work-holding devices.

For the first three exercises in this chapter you will need to operate a centre lathe with a three-jaw self-centring chuck already fitted. Later you will learn how to change work-holding devices.

A three-jaw chuck

The jaws of the three-jaw self-centring chuck are opened and closed by means of a chuck key inserted into one of the three square holes on the side of the chuck. When the chuck key is rotated all the jaws open or close together so that the work can be held centrally in the chuck. This type of chuck is only suitable for 'bright round bar' or 'bright hexagonal bar'.

Three-jaw chucks can not be relied on for concentricity if the workpiece is removed and returned to the chuck, so don't remove the workpiece until it is finished.

Safety – *always remove the chuck key before starting machine.*

Selection of spindle speeds

The spindle speed which the work should be rotated depends upon four factors:

- The diameter of the work being cut
- The type of material being cut
- The material from which the cutting tool is made
- Availability of coolant or cutting fluid

To calculate the correct spindle speed in rev/min for turning various materials, use the formula:

$$\text{Rev}/\text{min} = \frac{1000 \times S}{\pi \times d}$$

Where S = Cutting speed of the work material *
d = Work or drill diameter
π = 3·142, (often approximated to 3)

* See Appendix VII for the cutting speeds for various materials together with examples of spindle speed calculations. Some cutting tool manufacturers recommend different speeds to those quoted in Appendix VII.

Lathe cutting tool shapes

There are a number of different shapes of cutting tool suitable for use in a centre lathe. The cutting tool shape depends on the operation to be performed. Some of the most commonly used cutting tool shapes are shown and described below. All must be maintained with a keen cutting edge and re-sharpened or replaced if they become chipped.

Right-hand knife tool – used for machining light cuts on both faces or diameters. Although strength is limited, this tool shape is commonly used throughout industry as it is versatile.

Left-hand knife tool – used for removing material from the headstock side of the work. Useful for making concentric workpiece faces and diameters as the workpiece need not be removed from the chuck.

Chamfering tool – frequently used to cut chamfers on the corner of workpieces when the angle of the required chamfer is not critical. The chamfering tool shown on page 72 is being used to cut a 45° chamfer.

Roughing tools – used for large amount of material removal. The angle of the front face on the tool reduces the force on the tool by making the chips (pieces of swarf) thinner. Force reduction allows faster feed rates to be used. As the workpiece's corners will not be square, it must be followed with a finishing cut, usually with a right-hand knife tool.

Facing tool – similar in appearance to the right-hand knife tool but the distinguishing feature is the facing tool's point extends further to the left.
As its name suggests, it is first choice for facing the ends of workpieces.

Grooving tools – produced with special profiles to make grooves in workpieces which can locate other components. They usually have short cutting projections to increase their strength. An example of using a grooving tool to cut an 'O' ring groove is shown below.

Boring tools – available in a variety of shapes. The common feature of boring tools is a long shank which supports the cutting edge. The shank must be only as long as the hole is deep to reduce the effect of 'chatter' and vibration.

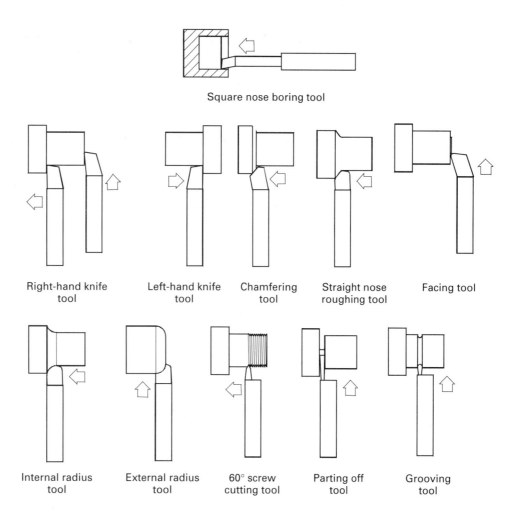

Square nose boring tool

Right-hand knife tool

Left-hand knife tool

Chamfering tool

Straight nose roughing tool

Facing tool

Internal radius tool

External radius tool

60° screw cutting tool

Parting off tool

Grooving tool

Radius tools – ground to suit the required radius of the corner of the workpiece. The drawings show a external radius tool and an internal radius tool in use.

Screw thread cutting tools – the angle of the sharp point of screw thread cutting tools is equal to the thread angle, usually 60°. The feed rate for single start threads is one pitch of the thread per chuck revolution.

Parting-off tool – used to separate the finished workpiece from the barstock. The parting-off tool is slowly fed into the workpiece's centre line.

Parting off is often a difficult operation; all moving parts should be clamped for maximum rigidity and you must take great care.

Machine centres

Machine centres are used on centre lathes for work-holding, supporting long workpieces and for setting cutting tools at the correct height.

A machine centre is a hardened steel 60° point mounted on a morse taper shank. When fitted into a morse tapered hole the point of the machine centre is on the centre line of the hole.

There are three types of machine centre in common use:

Full centre

General headstock and tailstock use

Half centre

For facing and small diameters

Rotating centre

For high speeds.

Setting the cutting tool in the tool post

The centre lathe cutting tool must be mounted in the tool post. Its cutting edge is adjusted to match the height of the spindle's centre line, this is said to be 'on centre'.

Setting the cutting tool on centre

The procedure is as follows:

(a) Insert a machine centre into the tailstock barrel. (Its point is a guide when adjusting tool height.)
(b) Clamp the cutting tool into the centre lathe's tool post with a minimum overhang (say 15 mm).
(c) Position the tool post so that the cutting tool's point faces the point of the machine centre.

Depending on the type of tool post fitted to your machine, you should then proceed by:

Either – Quick-change camlock tool post

(d) Slacken the grip of the hexagonal camlock handle.
(e) Turn the fine adjusting screw until the height of the cutting tool's point matches the height of the tailstock's centre.
(f) Lock the hexagonal camlock screw.
(g) Check that the height of the cutting tool's point still matches the height of the centre's point.

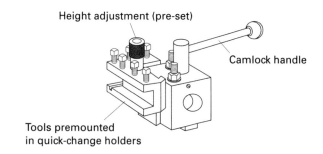

Height adjustment (pre-set)

Camlock handle

Tools premounted in quick-change holders

Quick to set cutting tool on centre, less rigid than four-way tool post

Or – Four-way turret tool post

(d) Insert or remove pieces of packing under the cutting tool to raise or lower its height. The height of the cutting tool's point should match the height of the tailstock's centre.
(e) Tighten the cutting tool in tool post.
(f) Check that the height of the cutting tool's point still matches the height of the centre's point.

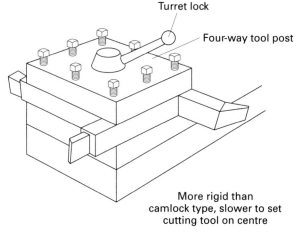

Turret lock

Four-way tool post

More rigid than camlock type, slower to set cutting tool on centre

Selecting a feed rate

The feed rate is the distance the cutting tool advances along the workpiece's surface for each revolution of the spindle. The feed rate affects the quality of surface finish of the workpiece, a fine feed (say 0·04 mm/rev) would give a better finish than a course feed (say 0·5 mm/rev). A course feed would remove material faster.

Usually a chart giving various feed rates for certain lever positions is on the headstock. The feed rate is set by adjusting the position of the levers. Use course feeds (0·5 mm/rev) for roughing out workpieces and fine feeds (0·04 mm/rev) for finishing accurately to size.

The shape of the tool nose also affects the surface finish.

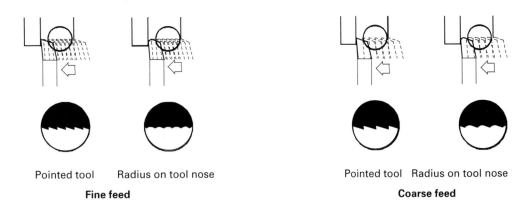

Pointed tool   Radius on tool nose   Pointed tool   Radius on tool nose
Fine feed   **Coarse feed**

Coolant and cutting fluid

Both coolants and cutting fluids are liquids used on centre lathes and other machine tools for:

1. Cooling the workpiece and the cutting tool.
2. Lubricating the cutting process.
3. Washing away pieces of swarf.
4. Improving the surface finish of the workpiece.
5. Preventing workpiece from corroding.

Coolant – Stored in a tank under the centre lathe and pumped out through a small pipe. The coolant can be directed onto the point at which the actual metal cutting takes place.

A common type of general purpose coolant is known as 'soluble oil'. Soluble oil is a thick oil mixed with water to form a milky coloured solution commonly called 'suds'.

Cutting fluid – For heavy duty work or for particularly long production runs, cutting fluids which have better lubricating properties than coolants are used. Mineral oils and synthetic oils are common cutting fluids. Cutting fluids are more expensive and efficient than soluble oil (coolant). Various blends of oils are suited to different cutting conditions. Particular cutting fluids are recommended for various applications.

Positioning of centre lathe guards

Turning can be a hazardous process. You must never touch moving workpieces or attempt to clear away swarf while the centre lathe is running. It is essential that guards are positioned and used appropriately when the machine is working to offer maximum protection for you, the operator.

1. **Centre lathe chuck guard**

   This is a popular type of chuck guard for centre lathes. The guard may be transparent so the workpiece can be seen. In the closed position it protects the operator from flying swarf and from being splashed by coolant.

   When hinged open there is easy access to the work area.

2. **Sliding lathe guard**

   This is a larger type of guard which is very efficient, protecting the turner from contacting the chuck and long workpieces as it guards the whole of the cutting area. It is simple to slide into position and is transparent.

   Electrical interlocks are sometimes fitted to sliding lathe guards to prevent machines from being started before the guard has been correctly positioned.

3. **Bellows guard**

   A bellows cover can be attached to the lathe to guard the lead screw and the feed shaft. This type of guard offers protection to the operator, by preventing loose clothing from entanglement, and protects the machine by keeping abrasive swarf away from precision components.

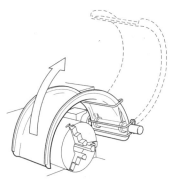

Centre lathe chuck guard

Sliding lathe guard

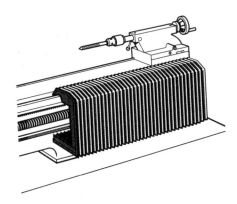

Bellows cover guarding the leadscrew and feed shaft

The Health and Safety at Work Act 1974 states that you must take reasonable care of the health and safety of yourself and other people who may be affected by your acts. This means you must *always* use guards provided and report any operating failures or damaged guards to your supervisor.

Operating the centre lathe

Safety
Never work on any machine until you have been shown how to operate it properly by a suitably qualified person.

Your supervisor will show you how to operate a centre lathe, including the:

- power supply and how to isolate it
- the various guards on the machine which you must use
- spindle stop, start and reverse controls
- hand feed dials on the handwheel for cross feed
- handwheels for cross feed and longitudinal feed
- power feed control for traversing along the work and surfacing across the work
- spindle speed selection levers
- feed selection levers
- coolant/cutting fluid supply
- clamps for the tailstock and the saddle
- emergency stop procedure.

*If you do not understand what you have been shown or if you are unsure how to proceed you must **ask!***

Safety
Never operate a machine until the slideways are clear and
all tools and equipment are away from moving machine parts.

Never leave a machine unattended whilst in motion.

When you have practised working the centre lathe using pieces of spare material, and have become confident with the controls, ask your supervisor for permission to start the turning exercise.

Exercise 3.1   *Turning exercise*

Complete the turning exercise using the procedure and tools indicated. Your finished work should be within the stated drawing limits.

On completion of the task, carefully measure your work and write in the table the actual sizes, noting any errors.

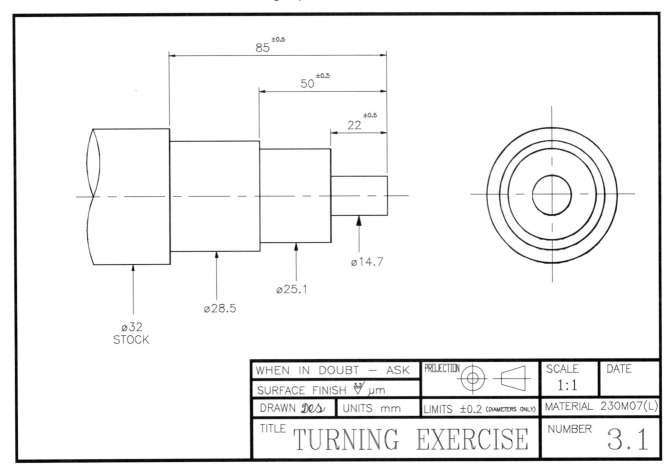

Planning

Procedure	Tools and equipment selected
1 Acquire material and check for size	Metric 300 mm rule
2 Hold work in a three-jaw chuck with 100 mm protruding	Centre lathe
3 Set spindle speed	Right-hand knife tool
4 Set cutting tool at machine's centre height	0 – 25 mm micrometer
5 Face off one end of the bar	25 – 50 mm micrometer
6 Turn each diameter, starting with the biggest	Centre (rotating or dead)
7 De-burr all sharp edges	$\frac{1}{2}$ lb hammer
8 Stamp your name on the end of your work	Letter stamps
9 Isolate your machine from the electricity supply	
10 Clean the work area and machine	

Complete the tables with the correct information.

Make of machine used:	**One graduation on the cross slide reduces the work's diameter by:**
Model of machine:	**Quantity of spindle speeds available on the machine:**
The machine centre height:	**Length of the tailstock barrel:**
The machine centre distance:	**The position of the automatic feed engagement lever:**
Maximum traverse length of the cross slide:	**Correct spindle speed for turning ø30 mm mild steel with HSS tooling:**
Maximum traverse length of the compound slide:	**Correct spindle speed for turning ø100 mm mild steel with HSS tooling:**

Write here the emergency stop system on the machine and state how it can be checked.

Sketch
Sketch a map of your workshop showing the location of the exits and any emergency stop buttons.

Finished inspection report

Component dimensions (mm)	Limits	Actual size	Error
Length 22	22.5 21.5		
ø28·5	28.7 28.3		
ø25·1	25.3 24.9		
ø15	14.9 14.5		
Remarks			

Results

Is the workpiece to the drawing specification?

Yes	No

If the completed workpiece is below drawing specification, write here the reasons for any errors, stating clearly how the errors will be avoided in future.

Start date	End date	Time taken (hours)	Signed satisfactory by supervisor

Thread cutting using dies

A simple and efficient method of cutting small external threads on a centre lathe is to use a circular split die in a diestock. The split die is mounted and set in the diestock as described on page 32. The front face of the tailstock barrel can be used to ensure the diestock is square to the workpiece.

Cutting external threads on a centre lathe using dies

The procedure is as follows:

(a) Ensure the outside diameter of the material to be threaded is the same as the thread's major (outside) diameter e.g. M10 = ø10 mm.

(b) Lightly chamfer the material's front face by setting the chamfering tool at the required angle as shown. The chamfer provides a lead which helps the die to start cutting the thread.

(c) Isolate centre lathe's electricity supply.

(d) Remove the cutting tool.

(e) Disengage the gearbox so that the spindle is free to turn.

(f) Set the diestock to cut at its maximum diameter (refer to fitting section page 32).

(g) Turn the tool post so that one of its plane surfaces faces the workpiece.

(h) Bring the tailstock up to the end of the workpiece and lock it to the bed with its front face about 20 mm away from the work.

(i) Position the diestock in the gap between the tailstock barrel and the workpiece.

(j) Move the barrel forward so that it *lightly* traps the diestock against the workpiece.

(k) Turn the handle of the diestock so that it rests on the tool post.

(l) Put a small amount of cutting oil on to the workpiece.

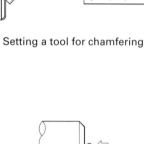

Setting a tool for chamfering

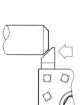

Chamfering the workpiece

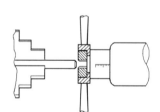

Set up ready to thread

Holding the die square

(m) Cut the thread by rotating the spindle with your left hand and gently move the tailstock barrel forward with your right hand keeping the diestock square to the workpiece.

(n) Move the tailstock barrel back each time you relieve the die of swarf (each half turn of the chuck).

(o) Continue thread cutting until the correct length is threaded.

(p) Check the thread with either thread gauges or the mating component if it is available.

(q) If necessary, the diestock can be reset with a screwdriver to finish the thread's profile.

Exercise 3.2   *Clamp studs*

Make the clamp studs using the procedure and tools indicated. Your finished work should be within the drawing limits.

On completion of the task, carefully measure your work and write in the table the actual sizes, noting any errors.

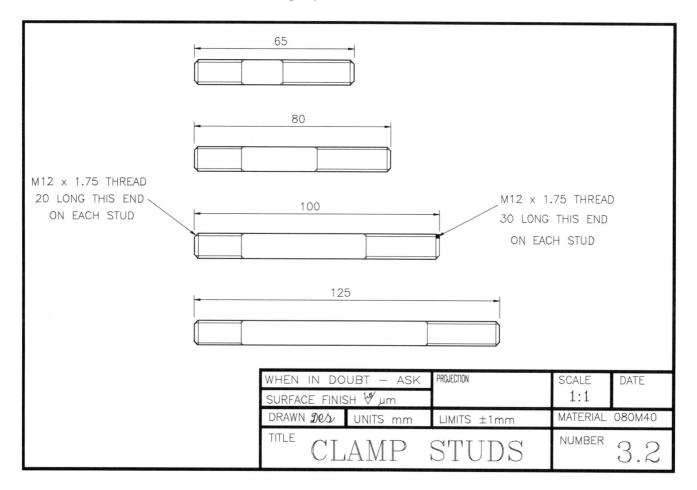

M12 x 1.75 THREAD
20 LONG THIS END
ON EACH STUD

M12 x 1.75 THREAD
30 LONG THIS END
ON EACH STUD

WHEN IN DOUBT — ASK	PROJECTION		SCALE 1:1	DATE
SURFACE FINISH ∇ μm				
DRAWN *Des*	UNITS mm	LIMITS ±1mm	MATERIAL 080M40	
TITLE CLAMP STUDS			NUMBER 3.2	

Planning

Procedure	Tools and equipment selected
1 Acquire material and check for size	Metric 300 mm rule
2 Saw length into pieces of approximate length	Hack saw
3 Set spindle speed	Centre lathe
4 Set cutting tool at machine's centre height	Right-hand knife tool
5 Face off ends to length	Centre (rotating or dead)
6 Chamfer the corners of the work with a chamfering tool	M12 x 1·75 split button die
7 Isolate your machine from the electricity supply	Diestock
8 Cut the thread to length with the stock and die	Screwdriver
9 Check the threads with a gauge	Thread gauge
10 Clean the work area and machine	

Research

Check the emergency stop switch works	How checked
Fire extinguishers	Types and where located
Clearing swarf	Facilities and where located

Write here four items of safety clothing to be used while doing the exercise
1   3
2   4

Sketch

Sketch a diestock. Show clearly how it is allows for adjustment for split button dies.

Finished inspection report

Component dimensions (mm)	Limits	Actual size	Error
M12 x 1·75 thread form	To fit M12 thread gauge		
Length of stud 1	66 64		
Length of stud 2	81 79		
Length of stud 3	101 99		
Length of stud 4	126 124		
Remarks			

Results

Is the workpiece to the drawing specification?

Yes	No

Is the completed workpiece below drawing specification?
Write here the reasons for any errors, stating clearly how the errors will be avoided in future.

Start date	End date	Time taken (hours)	Signed satisfactory by supervisor

Facing to length

When the overall length of a workpiece is specified with close limits, it is not possible to cut the length within the limits by using the scale on the longitudinal traverse handwheel. There are often no graduations on the longitudinal handwheel and when available they are quite coarse.

A reliable way to turn accurate lengths is as follows:

(a) Check the compound slide is parallel (set at 0°) to the lathe bed.
(b) Face both ends roughly to the correct length.
(c) Remove the workpiece from the chuck and measure it with a micrometer.
(d) Calculate the difference between the actual size and the required size.
(e) Put the workpiece back in the chuck and secure it.
(f) Set the compound slide's reading to zero.
(g) Turn the longitudinal handwheel until the tool *just* touches the end of the workpiece.
(h) Lock the carriage to the bed in this position with the locking screw/bolt.
(i) Feed the cutting tool point towards the chuck the calculated amount (stage (d)).
(j) Face the end off.
(k) The workpiece will now be the required length.

Chamfering

When cutting small chamfers on a lathe, a quick method is to use a chamfering tool. The angle of the front face of the cutting tool is set by turning the tool post so that the cutting tool's front face matches the blade of a protractor (see page 72 – the chamfering tool is set to 45° using a protractor).

With the workpiece secured in the machine, carefully feed the chamfering tool forward until the chamfer is formed to the specified length.

Lathe tool materials

Nearly all centre lathe cutting tools are made from either high-speed steel or tungsten carbide.

High-speed steel is cheaper and tougher (shock resistant) than tungsten carbide, and can be more easily shaped by grinding. High-speed steel is frequently used in manufacture of small quantities of components and development work. The high-speed steel cutting edge is fastened to a mild steel shank, usually by welding or by clamping it into a special tool holder.

Tungsten carbide is harder, more brittle and longer lasting than high-speed steel, allowing faster spindle speeds to be used. Tungsten carbide is frequently chosen for large batch production. The cutting tip, which is made from tungsten carbide is either clamped or permanently brazed to the tool's shank.

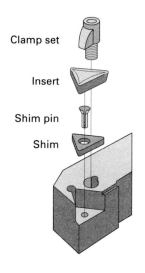

Clamp set

Insert

Shim pin

Shim

Clamped tungsten carbide tool
Very quick to change tip for a replacement

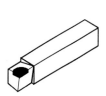

Brazed tungsten carbide tool
Brazed joint increases the toughness of the tool

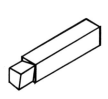

Welded HSS tool
HSS is an extremely tough cutting material

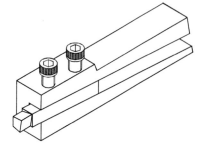

Clamped HSS tool
Economical cutting tool material

Angles on lathe cutting tools

Lathe cutting tools must be kept sharp or the surface finish of the work will be poor. When using a clamped tungsten carbide tip tool, if the tool tip becomes worn or chipped, a new tip edge can easily be fitted by unscrewing the old tip and either replacing it or turning it round.

Brazed tungsten tools and all types of high-speed steel tools must be re-sharpened by grinding. Your supervisor will usually do this for you.

All lathe cutting tools are ground in such a way as to avoid any part of the tool – except the actual cutting point – touching the workpiece. Consider the right-hand knife tool, the four important angles are:

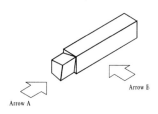

Arrow B

Arrow A

Right-hand knife cutting tool

Top rake
(15° for mild steel) angle of slope towards operator on top face of cutting tool

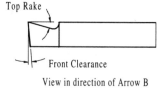

Top Rake

Front Clearance

View in direction of Arrow B

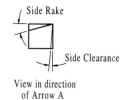

Side Rake

Side Clearance

View in direction of Arrow A

Front clearance
(8° for most materials) angle between front face of cutting tool and workpiece

Side rake
(15° for mild steel) angle of slope towards tailstock on top face of cutting tool

Side clearance
(6°–8° for most materials) angle between side face of cutting tool and workpiece

Note – rake angles should be increased for soft materials (e.g. aluminium) and decreased for hard materials (e.g. high carbon steel).

Defects on centre lathe cutting tools

When a cutting tool is not producing a satisfactory surface finish you should check the following before calling for assistance:

- The cutting tool height is correct.
- The spindle speed is correct.
- Coolant or cutting fluid is applied.

If the surface finish is still poor, check the actual point of the cutting tool's tip. It may be:

1. **Worn**
The cutting edge could be worn due to:

- regular 'wear and tear'
- incorrect height of tool point
- excessive spindle speeds
- lack of coolant or cutting fluid

2. **Chipped**
The corner of the cutting tip breaks usually as a result of either:

- tool point being knocked against another hard and sharp object e.g. another cutting tool, or
- intermittent cutting

3. **Burnt out**
If excessive friction is generated the heat causes the point of the cutting tool's tip to develop tiny thermal cracks which cause the tool point to burn out. This is often due to:

- excessive spindle speed
- lack of coolant or cutting fluid

4. **Built-up edge**
Particles of soft materials such as aluminium sometimes become welded onto the top surface of cutting tools, forming a built-up edge. It is caused by the heat generated by friction. The following actions can be taken to prevent built-up edges forming:

- Polish the top face of cutting tool.
- Increase rake angle of cutting tool.
- Use a more effective cutting fluid.

  If your cutting tool is defective in any of the above ways:

- Check the spindle speed is correct for the material being cut.
- Check the cutting tool is at centre height.
- Apply coolant or cutting fluid (if available).
- Ask your supervisor to sharpen the cutting tool point.
- Avoid using tungsten carbide tip cutting tools for intermittent cutting.

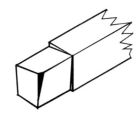

A worn out tool point – note the shiny edge

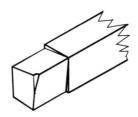

A chipped tool point

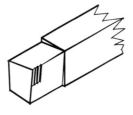

A burnt-out tool point

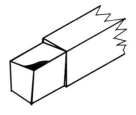

Built-up edge

Mounting cutting tools in the tailstock

The morse taper bore in the tailstock barrel can be used to mount the following:

- Machine centres, either rotating or 'dead'
- Drill chucks which can be used for holding centre drills, small parallel shank drills and reamers
- Drills with morse taper shanks, mounted directly into the tailstock barrel
- Machine reamers of various sizes
- Tapping heads

Once the workpiece is secured in the chuck, check that the morse tapered bore of the tailstock is clean and free from foreign matter. Wipe the outside of the drill's shank and push it firmly into the tailstock. If the tailstock morse taper does not match that of the drill's, a morse taper converting sleeve must also be used.

When a drilled or bored hole is required:

1. Start by centre drilling a small dimple in the end of the bar stock.

   (a) Mount a drill chuck in the tailstock
   (b) Fit a centre drill and set the machine spindle speed (see Appendix IV).
   (c) Lock the tailstock to the bed.
   (d) Carefully feed the barrel forward so that the centre drill cuts into the end of the workpiece.
   (e) The correct depth for a centre drilled hole is about $\frac{3}{4}$ of the way along centre drill's 60° point.

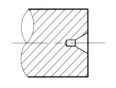

Centre drill depth correct

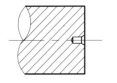

Centre drill not deep enough

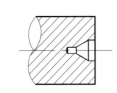

Centre drill too deep

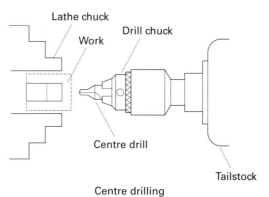

Lathe chuck

Work

Drill chuck

Centre drill

Tailstock

Centre drilling

2. To drill an accurately sized hole:

   (a) Select a drill to pilot drill (pre-drill) the workpiece with a smaller sized drill than the finished drill size. This will minimise the chances of the hole being oversized.

Fitting the drill

   (b) Mount the pilot drill in the tailstock securely.
   (c) Wind the tailstock handle until the measuring scale on the barrel reads zero.
   (d) Move the tailstock until the drill point touches the workpiece and lock the tailstock to the bed.
   (e) Start the centre lathe's spindle at the correct speed.
   (f) Apply coolant/cutting fluid.
   (g) Wind the drill forward until the correct depth is reached.

Drilling to depth

(h) Retract the drill from the newly drilled hole.
(i) Stop the spindle and remove the pilot drill.
(j) Fit the final size drill or reamer to finish the hole accurately to size (as stages (b)–(i) above).

Exercise 3.3 — *Drill stand legs*

Make the drill stand legs using the procedure and tools indicated. Your finished work should be within the drawing limits.

On completion of the task, carefully measure your work and write in the table the actual sizes, noting any errors.

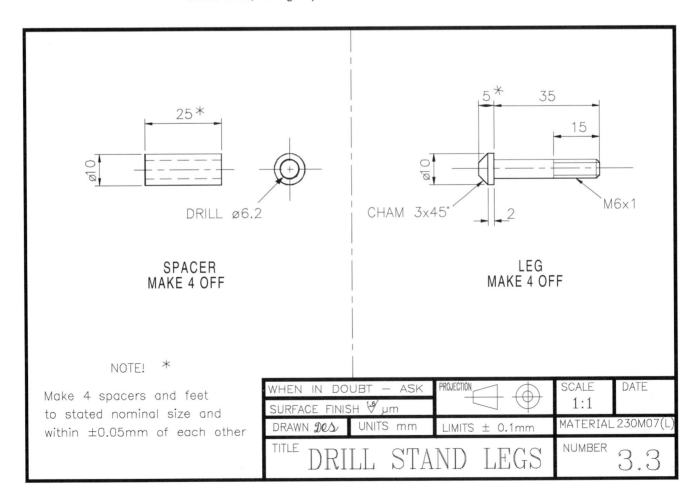

25 *

ø10

DRILL ø6.2

SPACER
MAKE 4 OFF

5 *   35

15

ø10

CHAM 3x45°   2

M6x1

LEG
MAKE 4 OFF

NOTE!   *

Make 4 spacers and feet
to stated nominal size and
within ±0.05mm of each other

WHEN IN DOUBT — ASK	PROJECTION	SCALE	DATE
SURFACE FINISH ∀ µm		1:1	
DRAWN *Des*	UNITS mm	LIMITS ± 0.1mm	MATERIAL 230M07(L)
TITLE DRILL STAND LEGS			NUMBER 3.3

Planning

Procedure	Tools and equipment selected
Spacers 1 Acquire material and check for size 2 Saw four pieces for spacers 26 mm long at a bench vice 3 Face both ends of each spacer to length within ±0·05 mm 4 Centre drill and drill through each spacer in turn **Legs** 1 Acquire material and check for size 2 Saw into two pieces, each approximately 90 mm long 3 Turn ø6 x 35 mm long on each end of material 4 Cut M6 x 1 thread, 15 mm long on each end of each piece 5 Saw each piece in half at a bench vice 6 Turn ends to 5 mm ±0·05 mm shoulder 7 Cut chamfers on legs with a chamfering tool 8 Remove all burrs from the workpieces 9 Isolate machine and clean the work area	Hacksaw Metric 300 mm rule Metric 0–25 micrometer Centre drill Drill chuck Chamfering tool Ø6·2 drill Right-hand knife tool M6 x 1 stock & die

Complete the tables with the correct information.

Number of different power feed rates available	Coarsest feed	Feed rate used	Finest feed
Location of lever which engages power feed	How is power feed switched from cross feed to longitudinal feed?		
Drilling spindle speed selected	How selected		

Write three reasons why it is important that the area around the centre lathe is kept clean and tidy

1

2

3

Sketch

Sketch the lathe chuck guard.

Finished inspection report

Component dimensions (mm)	Limits	Actual size				Error			
1 Spacer lengths	25.05 24.95								
2 Foot lengths	5.05 4.95								
3 Plain lengths	35.1 34.9								
4 Hole diameter	6.2 6.0								
Remarks									

Results

Are the workpieces within the drawing specification?   Yes   No

If the completed workpiece is below drawing specification, write here the reasons for any errors, stating clearly how the errors will be avoided in future.

Start date	End date	Time taken (hours)	Signed satisfactory by supervisor

Work-holding devices

There are five different types of work-holding device commonly used on centre lathes:

1. Three-jaw self-centring chuck
2. Four-jaw independent chuck
3. Face plate
4. Catch plate (for turning between centres)
5. Spring collets

The applications and uses for these work-holding devices are described below.

1. Three-jaw self-centring chuck

This is the most widely used chuck on a centre lathe. It can only be used to hold bright round barstock, bright hexagonal barstock or previously turned components.

Insert the chuck key in the square and turn it clockwise; all three jaws move in together to grip the workpiece. Female jaws can be used to hold large diameter workpieces.

The drawback with this type of chuck is that if a workpiece is removed and replaced back into the chuck, the workpiece no longer runs exactly true (concentric). There is no means to correct this run out.

Three-jaw self-centring chuck
The jaws are opened and closed with the chuck key

When changing the jaws, ensure the set of jaws you are going to fit are an actual set (they are usually numbered with a code). The slots on the front face of the chuck and each jaw are numbered 1, 2 and 3. Make sure that jaw No 1 goes into slot No 1 and is 'picked up' by the scroll first, then insert jaw No 2 in slot No 2, etc.

Safety – *Never leave a chuck key in a chuck when not in use. If the machine is started with the chuck key in, the chuck key will fly out causing injury or damage.*

2. Four-jaw independent chuck

The jaws of this type of chuck are each adjusted independently to grip the workpiece. Workpieces of any constant cross-sectional shape (e.g. square, octagon, or black round bar) can be accurately gripped if it is set up with the aid of a dial test indicator.

Four-jaw chucks are used for holding part-finished work which must run absolutely true; however, they are slow to set up.

3. Face plate

The face plate is used for holding large irregular-shaped workpieces. The workpiece is bolted onto the face plate through its slots. Sometimes counterbalance weights are necessary to ensure the smooth running of the machine. They must be *securely* fixed to the face plate for safety.

Face plates are only used for short workpieces and are very slow to set up.

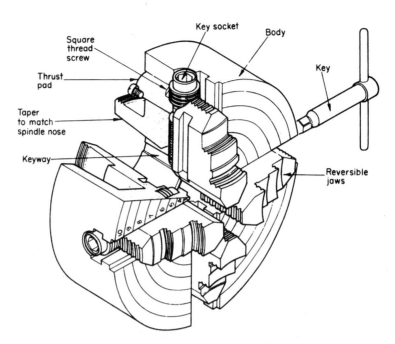

Four-jaw independent chuck

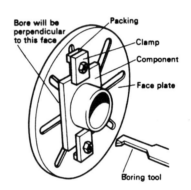

Face plate

4. Catch plate

The catch plate has a peg or slot which transmits the rotary drive to the workpiece via a carrier when it is held between centres (see page 84).

Work is normally held in this way when all the diameters must be concentric and it is to be machined all over.

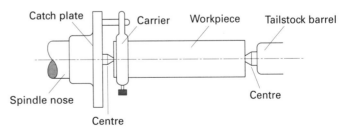

Work holding between centres

5. Spring collets

Spring collets can be used for holding workpieces when a higher degree of concentricity is required than provided by a three-jaw chuck. They also cause little damage to the workpiece's surface.

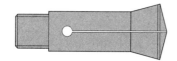

Spring collet

Spring collets are special inserts which may be inserted into the centre lathe's spindle. When the operator pulls a lever (or turns a handwheel), the spring collet is drawn back into the taper of the lathe's spindle, closing up and gripping the workpiece.

Changing the work-holding device

As introduced earlier, there are a number of different methods of attaching the work-holding device to the machine's spindle. Each machine tool manufacturer has slightly different designs of spindle, the two most common methods being the screwed type and the cam lock type.

The work-holding device can be changed quite quickly and easily, your supervisor will show you the correct method of changing them on your type of machine.

Be sure to:

Correct lifting technique
Bend at the knees and keep your head well up

(a) isolate the machine at the mains before starting
(b) use correct lifting technique when handling heavy chucks
(c) adequately protect the machine bed from damage by use of a piece of wood called a chuck board or similar device
(d) replace chucks to the appropriate storage rack, keeping them away from gangways/emergency exits
(e) thoroughly clean the spindle nose and mating faces on the chuck before assembly
(f) tighten the work-holding device securely before starting the machine
(g) check the chuck runs true on both its front face and its periphery (outside edge) before turning the centre lathe on

Turning between centres

When a workpiece is specified as requiring concentric diameters and it cannot be completed in one setting in a lathe chuck, the most efficient method of turning it is to hold it between the lathe centres.

The procedure is as follows:

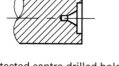

A protected centre drilled hole

(a) Centre drill the workpiece at both ends, either on a centre lathe using a three-jaw chuck or in a drilling machine. The centre drilled holes form a 60° surface for the centres to locate on. It is good practice to protect the centre with a small recess.
(b) Mount the centre lathe's catch plate in the spindle nose.

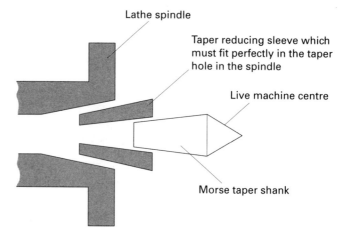

Mounting the headstock centre

(c) Clean a centre and insert it into the morse tapered hole in the spindle nose (a special bush is often required to convert morse taper sizes). This centre is called a

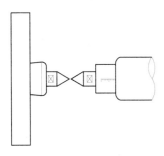

Checking centre alignment

'live centre' because it rotates with the spindle. The point of the centre is now exactly in line with the spindle's axis.

(d) Clean and insert a centre into the tailstock barrel.

(e) Move the two centres together so that their points nearly touch. If there is an alignment error (i.e. if points don't match) see your supervisor; the tailstock may need adjustment.

(f) Select a lathe carrier which fits the workpiece's outside diameter and connects to receive drive from the catch plate. There are two types of carrier:

- cranked tail carriers for slotted catch plates
- straight tail carriers for catch plates with driving pegs

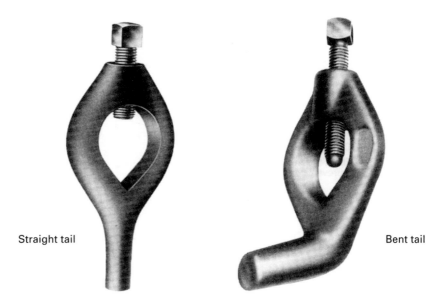

Straight tail   Bent tail

Two types of lathe carrier

(g) Attach the carrier to the headstock end of the workpiece.

(h) Clean the centre points and centre holes in the workpiece.

(i) Set the tailstock barrel with about 60 mm to 80 mm protruding from the tailstock body.

(j) Lock the tailstock to the bed in a position allowing a gap between the centres slightly greater than the length of the workpiece.

(k) Put the left-hand end of the workpiece in the headstock centre and wind the tailstock barrel forward until the tailstock centre supports the right-hand end of the workpiece.

(l) Apply some graphite lubricant to the tailstock centre to stop it overheating.

(m) Check that the carrier is receiving drive from the catch plate.

(n) Lock the carrier into position on the workpiece; the workpiece should be able to rock a little.

(o) Check that the workpiece has no end float.

(p) Lock the tailstock barrel in position.

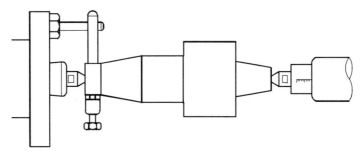

Workpiece mounted between centres

Taper turning using the compound slide

The compound slide of a centre lathe can be swivelled and fixed at any angle to the spindle. When the compound slide is set at an angle the cutting tool can then be manually wound forward along the angular compound slide generating a taper on the workpiece. Offsetting the compound slide is a simple and effective method of turning tapers which are too long to be turned with a form tool. A good finish is only achieved by carefully winding the cutting tool forward slowly and steadily.

The length of taper turned by this method is restricted to the length of the compound slide. Most centre lathes' compound slides are limited to about 125 mm long, so this would be the maximum length of taper which could be turned.

The procedure is as follows:

(a) Look at the drawing and notice if the angle on the workpiece is indicated as the included angle or the angle per side.

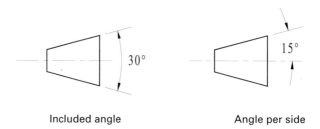

Included angle   Angle per side

(b) If the angle indicated on the drawing is the included angle, it must be halved to find the angle per side.
(c) Set the cutting tool on centre height.

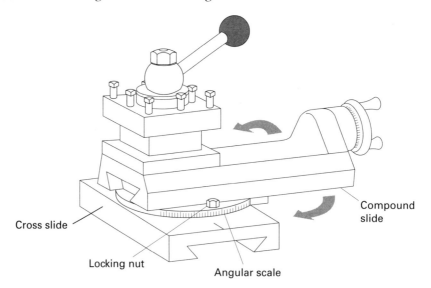

Setting the compound slide angle

(d) Turn the compound slide to half of the included angle.
(e) Wind the compound slide out as far as it will go.
(f) Turn the tool post so that the tool is straight.
(g) Move the tool with the cross slide so that it is near to the end of the workpiece.
(h) Lock the saddle to the bed.
(i) Start the machine's spindle.
(j) Apply a 'cut' with the cross slide handwheel.
(k) Feed the tool forward with the compound slide handwheel slowly and steadily.
(l) When the tool stops cutting, wind the compound slide back to the start.
(m) Repeat stages (j) to (l) until the taper is as required.

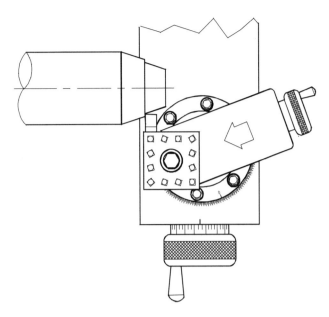

Taper turning using the compound slide

Clutch tool body

Make the clutch tool body. You must plan the tools required and an operation sequence before starting work.

Your finished work should be within the drawing limits. On completion of the task, carefully measure your work and write in the table the actual sizes, noting any errors.

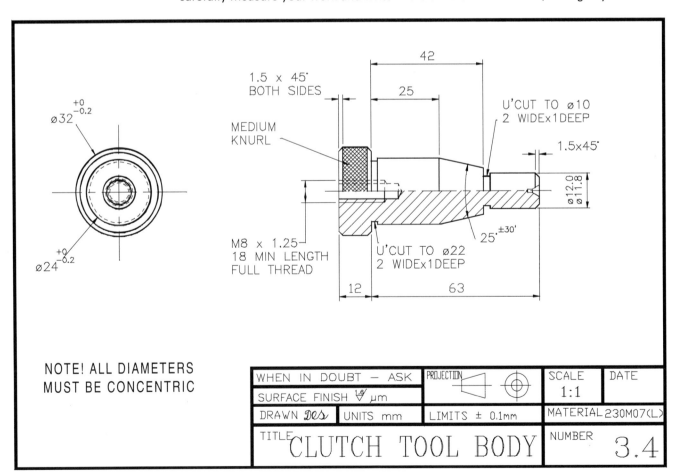

Planning

Procedure
1 Acquire material and check for size
2 Face to length and centre drill both ends
3 Hold between centres
4 Turn all diameters concentric
5 Turn 25° taper
6 Chamfer all corners
7 Hold in 3-jaw self-centring chuck
8 Drill hole, tap the M8 x 1.25 thread
9 Knurl the outside
10 De-burr the workpiece and clean the work area

Tools and equipment selected

Research

Angular movement turned for each compound slide graduation	How measured
Maximum taper length available using the compound slide	**How measured**
Angle at which compound slide is set for taper on the exercise	**How selected**
Name of lubricant applied to tailstock centre	**Reason for application of lubricant**

Write here the **safety procedures** to be observed particular to the task.

1

2

3

Sketch

Make a sketch showing the mechanism for locking the compound slide in position.

Finished inspection report

Component dimensions (mm)		Limits	Actual size	Error
ø12		12·0 mm 11·8 mm		
ø24		24·0 mm 23·8 mm		
Root diameter of undercuts	ø10	9·9 mm 12·1 mm		
	ø22	21·9 mm 22·1 mm		
25° angle		25°30' 24°30'		
Length 12 mm		12·1 mm 11·9 mm		
Remarks				

Results

Is the workpiece to the drawing specification?

Yes		No

If the completed workpiece is below drawing specification, write here the reasons for any errors, stating clearly how the errors will be avoided in future.

Start date	End date	Time taken (hours)	Signed satisfactory by supervisor

Boring on a centre lathe

A process known as boring is carried out on a centre lathe when an existing hole is to be accurately finished to a specific size. The technique is particulary useful for machining unusual sized holes if a reamer is not available, or finishing internal diameters when concentricity in essential.

Components being bored cannot be mounted between centres, but any of the other work-holding devices described on page 82 would be suitable. The cutting tool used for boring must be selected as follows:

1. **Types of boring tool in common use:**

   (a) **Butt welded high-speed steel boring tools** Useful for a variety of tool room and specialist tasks, the shape of the cutting edge can be ground for individual requirements.

Butt welded, high-speed steel boring tool

   (b) **Carbide-tipped boring tools** The carbide tip is secured in the tool holder by a small screw. The tip's hardness allows fast cutting speeds to be used. The tool's cutting angles can not be ground to suit particular cutting conditions, consequently carbide tipped boring tools are used for batch production.

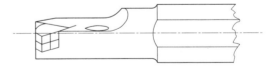

Carbide-tipped boring tool

2. **Boring tool length** The length of tool overhang must be kept to a minimum so that there is the least chance of setting up any vibration and 'chatter'.
3. **Boring tool clearance** Tool angles, particularly clearance angle must be carefully checked before starting to cut metal.

   Examine the two figures. Although the boring tool used is the same in both drawings, the workpiece is smaller on the bottom drawing. Notice that the heel of the boring tool fouls (catches) the smaller workpiece on the bottom drawing. If this is the case the corner of the tool is removed by grinding.

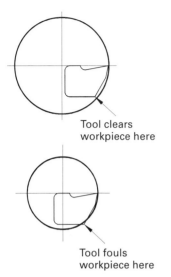

Tool clears
workpiece here

Tool fouls
workpiece here

Boring tool viewed 'in situ'
through the machine spindle

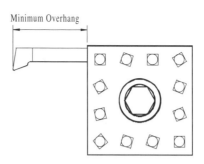

Setting a boring tool

On the larger bore, the boring tool doesn't foul the workpiece at all.

A good position to see if a boring tool is fouling a workpiece is to look through the spindle's bore and view the boring tool inside the workpiece.

Boring

The procedure is as follows:

(a) The workpiece is mounted in a suitable work-holding device, centre drilled and drilled to 'rough out' the hole. Usually this roughing out takes the bore to within about 3 mm of the finished size.

(b) Mount the boring tool in the tool post on centre height with minimum overhang.

(c) Position the lathe's saddle and cross slide so that the boring tool point is touching the near corner of the workpiece.

Setting centre height

(d) Check there is clearance under the cutting edge.

(e) Calculate and set the correct rev/min for the spindle (use the finished bore diameter as the work diameter).

$$\text{Rev/min} = \frac{1000 \times S}{\pi \times d}$$

(f) Wind the boring tool towards you (i.e. backwards) so that it is ready to take a cut.

(g) Start the machine's spindle.

(h) Feed the boring tool into the workpiece. If the bore goes completely through the workpiece, power feed can be used (see Note 1 below).

(i) Wind the saddle back so that the boring tool is clear of the workpiece.

(j) Measure the bore size using either:
   (i) internal micrometers (for large bores)
   (ii) telescopic gauges (for small bores)

(k) Apply roughing and finishing cuts with the cross slide handwheel to take roughing and finishing cuts until you have completed the boring operation.

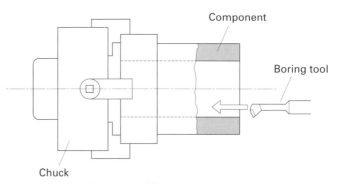

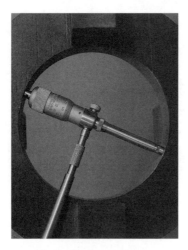

Boring on a centre lathe

Measuring bore with an
internal micrometer

Measuring bore with
'telescopic bore gauges'

Notes

1. The use of stops will assist with boring features to depth and turning accurate
   lengths. Ask your supervisor if stops are available for the bed of your centre lathe,
   he will show you how to fit and use them.
2. If stops are not available, and the depth of a bore is specified, the saddle should be
   locked to the bed. The depth of bore can then be determined by winding the
   compound slide forward while reading its dial.
3. The boring tool sometimes deflects slightly during cutting. When this happens the
   bore in workpiece is left slightly oversize. If this is happening and your workpiece
   is near to the finished size, repeat the pass at the same cross slide setting. The
   boring tool will not deflect on the second pass, so the size will be as expected.

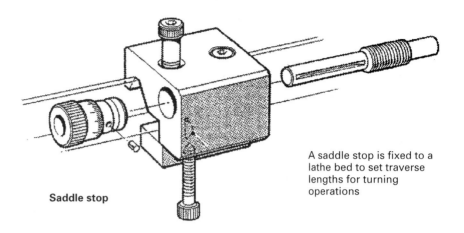

A saddle stop is fixed to a lathe bed to set traverse lengths for turning operations

Saddle stop

The mandrel

A mandrel is a round bar which is slightly tapered. It is pressed into a hole in a workpiece and mounted between centres on a lathe. The workpiece can then be machined on its outside surfaces in such a way that the outside diameter is concentric with the inside diameter. Mandrels are used when an outside diameter is to be turned concentric to its bore e.g. when turning a pulley.

The key features of a mandrel are:

- centre holes at each end are large and recessed
- ground surface finish machined from the centre holes
- slight taper of about 0·5 mm per metre (0·0005" taper per inch)
- usually a '+' sign is etched on mandrels at the bigger end

Mounting a workpiece on a mandrel

(a) Select a mandrel to fit the bored (or reamed) workpiece.
(b) Remove all burrs from the workpiece.
(c) Insert the small end of the mandrel into the workpiece's bore.
(d) Use a mandrel press to firmly push the mandrel into the workpiece's bore.

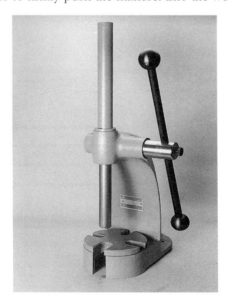

A mandrel press

When turning with a mandrel, mount the mandrel with its large end (marked +) at the headstock end of the centre lathe (this tends to keep the workpiece tight).

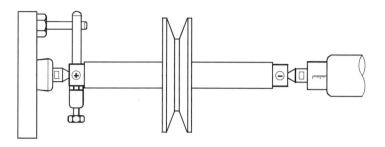

A pulley mounted on a mandrel ready for turning between centres

The turning process is the same as turning between centres. The carrier is attached to a flat on the end of the mandrel; however, it is advisable to take smaller depths of cut as the work could slide on the mandrel.

Exercise 3.5   *Boring exercise*

Make the boring exercise using the procedure and tools indicated. Your finished work should be within the drawing limits. On completion of the task, carefully measure your work and write in the table the actual sizes, noting any errors.

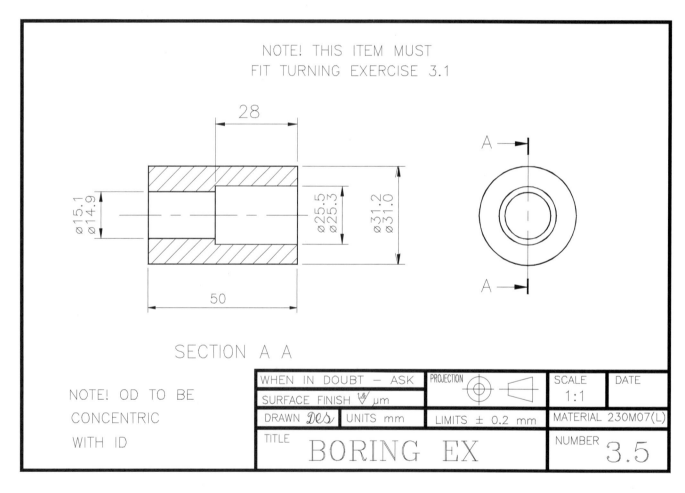

Planning

Procedure
1 Acquire material and check for size
2 Face the ends to length in a three-jaw chuck
3 Centre drill, drill and ream hole through
4 Bore ø25 mm hole to depth
5 Remove three-jaw chuck
6 Mount catch plate and centres
7 Mount workpiece on mandrel
8 Turn outside diameter concentric to bore
9 De-burr and check sizes
10 Isolate and clean machine

Tools and equipment selected
Centre lathe
Ø 15 mandrel
Right-hand knife tool
0 – 25 micrometer
25 – 50 micrometer
Telescopic gauges
Boring tool

Research

State how bed is protected from damage when changing chucks	**How used**
Difference between large and small diameter on mandrel	**Details of measurements**
Centre lathe spindle speed for reaming	**How selected**

Write here the **safety procedures** to be observed when changing the work holding device
1
2
3

Sketch

Make a series of sketches to show how to lift a heavy load correctly.

Finished inspection report

Complete the chart for all sections.

Component dimensions (mm)	Limits	Actual size	Error
1 Overall length			
2 Outside diameter			
3 Bore diameter			
4 Bore depth			
5 Reamed hole diameter			
Remarks			

Results

Is the workpiece to the drawing specification? | Yes | | No |

If the completed workpiece is below drawing specification, write here the reasons for any errors, stating clearly how the errors will be avoided in future.

Start date	End date	Time taken (hours)	Signed satisfactory by supervisor

Knurling

A knurl is a straight or diamond indented pattern which provides a thumb grip on the outside of screwed components. A knurl is put on a surface with a knurling tool which has two small high speed steel wheels which are forced onto the workpiece's surface, reshaping it to form the pattern.

Two types of knurling tools are commonly available as shown below.

Caliper type knurling tool   Pivot head or plunge type knurling tool

Method of using the caliper type knurling tool

(a) The knurling tool is secured in the lathe tool post with the jaws square to the axis of the work. If necessary, the work should be supported by the tailstock centre.

(b) Adjust the cross slide of the centre lathe to position the knurling wheels diametrically over the workpiece.

(c) With the cam handle vertical, close the wheels by means of the adjusting screw until the wheels contact the workpiece. If a number of the same components are to be knurled, the adjusting screw should be locked with the locknut.

(d) With the centre lathe running at a moderate speed, pull the cam handle down until a distinct form appears on the workpiece. Traverse the wheels slowly along the workpiece using coolant.

(e) For higher quality knurling, release the cam at the end of the first pass and repeat the operation, this time using light pressure and higher work speed. A clean well-formed knurl will result.

A caliper knurling tool operating on a precision centre lathe

Tapping

Tapping (cutting internal threads with taps) can be carried out on a centre lathe either:

1. by hand, using hand taps and a tap wrench
   or
2. using machine taps with special machine taps in a tapping head

Tapping on a centre lathe by hand

The process is as follows:

(a) Face off the end of the workpiece.
(b) Centre drill the end of the workpiece deep enough to chamfer the hole and provide a lead ready for tapping.
(c) Drill the workpiece with the appropriate tapping size drill (see Appendix III) to the required depth. If a 'blind hole' is being prepared, drill it 4 or 5 mm deeper than the minimum thread length.
(d) Switch off the electricity supply at the mains.

For taps with a centre hole:

(e) Insert a centre into the tailstock.
(f) Select a suitable size tap wrench and mount the taper tap in the wrench.
(g) Apply tapping compound to the tap.
(h) Position the tool post so that its plain edge is facing the workpiece.
(i) Locate the tap wrench handle on the flat of the tool post and the end of the tap in the tailstock centre.
(j) Insert the front of the tap in the mouth of the drilled hole.
(k) Put the machine in neutral gear.
(l) Turn the chuck carefully by hand to cut the thread, relieving the chips frequently and maintaining *light* pressure on the tap with the tailstock.
(m) For deep holes, remove the tap occasionally to clear the chips.
(n) Manually turn the chuck backwards to remove the tap.
(o) Insert the second tap and finish the thread.
(p) Use the plug tap only to finish blind holes to full depth.

The set up for hand tapping on a centre lathe

For taps without a centre hole:

Complete stages (a) – (d) as above, then continue as follows:
(e) Mount a drill chuck in the tailstock.
(f) Fit the taper tap in the drill chuck.
(g) Apply tapping compound to the tap.
(h) Insert the front of the tap in the mouth of the drilled hole.
(i) Put the machine in neutral gear.
(j) Turn chuck carefully by hand and allow the tailstock to slide along the bed (this starts thread square to workpiece's axis).
(k) After the first 3 or 4 threads are cut remove the taper tap from the drill chuck.
(l) Transfer taper tap to a tap wrench, complete stages (m) – (p) for taps with a centre hole (above).

Machine tapping on a centre lathe

Special tap holders called tapping heads and machine taps are necessary for machine tapping.

Machine tapping head

A machine tapping head enables tapping to be carried out using a machine's power.
   Special machine taps are needed when using a tapping head.
   The tapping head holds the tap square to the workpiece being threaded.

Machine tapping head

Machine taps

Machine taps are stronger than hand taps, having an angled cutting face which forces swarf to the front of the tap.
   For cutting blind holes, a spiral helix tap like the one shown here should be used. Its flutes are designed to direct swarf out of the hole.

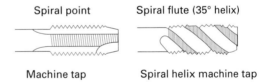

Spiral point   Spiral flute (35° helix)

Machine tap   Spiral helix machine tap

The process for machine tapping is:

(a) Face off the end of the workpiece.
(b) Centre drill the workpiece to the same diameter as the finished thread, this gives a slight lead.
(c) Drill the workpiece with the appropriate tapping size drill to the required depth, if a blind hole is being prepared, drill it 4 or 5 mm deeper than the minimum thread length.
(d) Select the machine tap to suit the process.
(e) Consult the tap manufacturer's data book and set the centre lathe's spindle speed.
(f) Insert the tap holder into the tailstock's morse taper barrel.
(g) Insert the tap in the tap holder.
(h) With the spindle operating, wind the tailstock forwards, entering the tap into the hole.

(i) The cutting process will draw the tap into the hole and when the cutting force becomes excessive or the tap 'bottoms', a friction clutch then allows the tap to turn in the tapping head.

(j) Reverse the direction of rotation of the spindle and the tap will be extracted from the hole.

(k) If the tap becomes excessively tight, it can be removed, cleaned and more tapping compound applied. Repeat the process to finish tapping the hole through.

Parting off

When parts have been machined on the end of long barstock it is sometimes beneficial to cut the finished workpiece off the barstock in the lathe with a parting-off tool.

The parting-off tool is fed in behind the completed work and cuts a groove behind it which separates the finished workpiece from the barstock.

The cutting tool used may be a special tungsten tipped tool, a HSS welded tip tool or an inserted blade type.

The process is quite tricky because parting-off tools are relatively thin and fragile, consequently special care is needed when parting off.

Parting-off tool tips are available 'handed', which refers to the slope on the tool's front edge. If it slopes to the left, the workpiece will be left with a pip; if it slopes to the right, the barstock will be left with a pip. Neutral tools are also available.

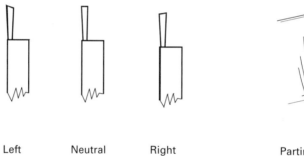

Left   Neutral   Right

Parting off a workpiece in a centre lathe

Before parting off:

Always ensure the machine is as rigid as possible, this means:

- Work is held securely in a chuck (you can not part off work that is held between centres).
- The workpiece should protrude a minimum amount from the chuck.
- The parting-off tool has a minimum overhang over the tool post.
- The parting-off tool's blade length is only slightly more than the work's radius.
- The compound slide is near to the middle of its travel.
- The saddle is locked to the bed with the screw on top of the carriage (where possible).

Always ensure the machine is set up correctly, this means:

- The parting-off tool is sharp and set at the correct centre height.
- The spindle speed is slower than calculated for normal turning, half speed is advised.
- The side of the parting-off tool is square to the workpiece, this prevents its sides 'binding' on the sides of the workpiece as it feeds into the groove.
- Ensure there is plenty of coolant available (except for cast iron which doesn't need coolant).
- The guards are in place.

Safety – *when parting off it is particulary important to wear safety glasses and to concentrate well on what you are doing.*

The procedure is as follows:

(a) Line up the parting-off tool's right-hand edge with the required end of the workpiece.
(b) Start the spindle and feed the parting-off tool into the workpiece constantly and carefully.
(c) Reduce the feed rate as the parting-off tool point nears the centre of the workpiece.
(d) The workpiece will fall into the coolant tray.
(e) Turn off the spindle before removing the workpiece from the coolant tray.

Exercise 3.6   *Depth gauge parts*

Plan the manufacture of the depth gauge parts listing the procedure and tools to be used. When your supervisor has approved your plan, make the three components in your planned sequence.

On completion of the task, carefully measure your work and write in the table the actual sizes, noting any errors.

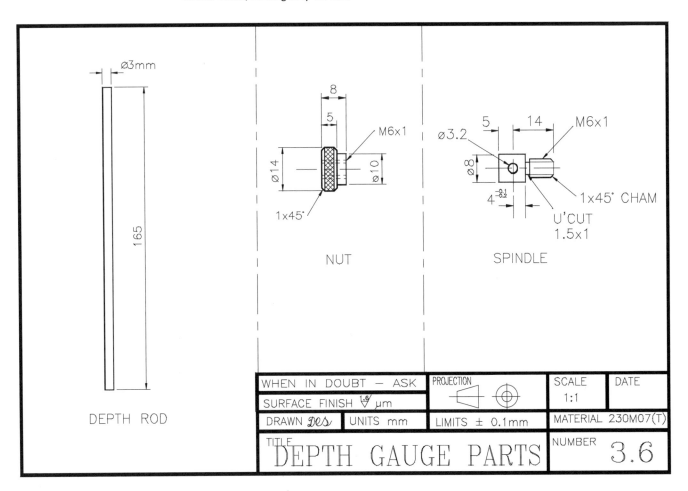

Planning

Procedure	Tools and equipment selected
1 Acquire material and check for size	
2	
3	
4	
5	
6	
7	
8	
9 De-burr and inspect for size	
10 Isolate and clean the machine	

Research

Work-holding device used	How selected
Amount of workpiece protruding during spindle manufacture	Reason for minimum amount of workpiece protrusion
How to confirm the chuck jaws used are a matching set	Details of set

Write here the **safety procedures** to be observed particular to the task.

1

2

3

Sketch

Make two sketches of a three-jaw chuck holding a workpiece. One sketch must show male (internal) jaws, the other must show female (external) jaws.

Holding a workpiece in male (internal) jaws	Holding a workpiece in female (external) jaws

Finished inspection report

Complete the chart for all sections

Component dimensions (mm)	Limits	Actual size	Error
Spindle body length			
Spindle body diameter			
Nut length			
Nut ø10			
Thread assembly	–	–	
Rod length			
Remarks			

Results

Is the workpiece to the drawing specification? | **Yes** | | **No** |

If completed workpiece is below drawing specification, write here the reasons for any errors, stating clearly how the errors will be avoided in future.

Start date	End date	Time taken (hours)	Signed satisfactory by supervisor

Setting work in a four-jaw chuck with a dial test indicator

When turning a long irregular workpiece in a centre lathe, the four-jaw chuck is the best work-holding device. The outside diameter can be turned and there is access to the end of the workpiece.

Care must be taken to set up the workpiece centrally in the chuck jaws so that the workpiece is located centrally. If you are making a workpiece which must be eccentric (e.g. a crankshaft) it can be held in a four-jaw chuck and set to the appropriate eccentricity.

Setting a workpiece in a four-jaw chuck

(a) Turn off the centre lathe at the mains electricity supply.
(b) Put the workpiece in the four-jaw chuck. Tighten the jaws so that they are all in a similar position relating to the concentric grooves on the chuck's front face.
(c) Stand a scribing block (or a surface gauge) on the machine's cross slide and adjust its point to touch the workpiece.

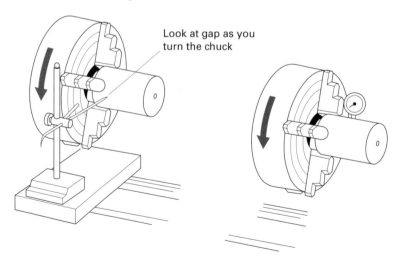

Look at gap as you turn the chuck

Surface gauge set on top of cross slide

Using a dial test indicator to set a workpiece accurately in a four-jaw chuck

(d) Manually turn the chuck and observe which part of the workpiece is closest to the scribe (the high spot).

(e) Slacken the jaw nearest the high spot and tighten the jaw opposite moving the workpiece closer to the chuck's centre line.

(f) Repeat this process until the workpiece is touching the scribe all the time and all the chuck jaws are tight.

To set the workpiece more accurately, a dial test indicator can be used to measure any eccentricity.

(g) Remove the scribing block (or the surface gauge) and replace it with a dial test indicator standing on a magnetic base.

(h) Set the dial test indicator so that its stylus touches the workpiece.

(i) Slowly rotate the chuck by hand as before. You will see the dial test indicator's pointer shows the workpiece's eccentricity on its calibrated face.

(j) The work setting procedure is the same as stage (e) – (f) above, but the sensitivity of the dial test indicator will ensure that the workpiece is set more accurately. It is possible to set the workpiece concentric to within 0·02 mm.

Ensure all the jaws are tight and continue as you would if you were working as normal.

Exercise 3.7   *Toolmakers clamp screws*

Write a planning sequence for manufacture of the toolmakers clamp screws.
On completion of the task, carefully measure your work and write in the table the actual sizes, noting any errors. Your finished work should be within the drawing limits.

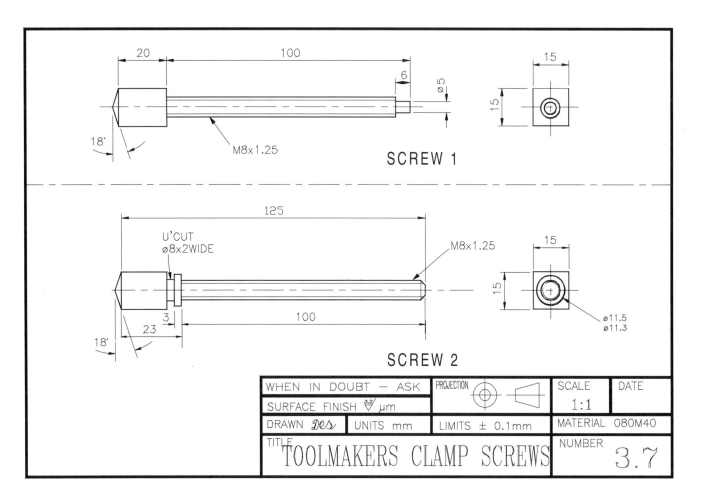

Planning

Procedure	Tools and equipment selected
1 Acquire material and check for size	
2	
3	
4	
5	
6	
7	
8	
9 Isolate and clean the machine	

Research

Type of centre used in tailstock	How selected
Turning cutting tools selected	**Details of tools material and shape**
Work holding device used	**Reason for selection**
Type of chuck jaws used	**Reason for selection**

Write here the **safety procedures** to be observed particular to the task.

1

2

3

Sketch

Sketch a set-up showing a dial test indicator in use for checking a three-jaw chuck face is running true.

Finished inspection report

Complete the chart for all sections.

Component dimensions (mm)	Limits	Actual size	Error
Undercut width			
Undercut depth			
Thread profile	To fit thread gauge		
ø5 mm end			
Remarks			

Results

Is the workpiece to the drawing specification?

Yes		**No**

If the completed workpiece is below drawing specification, write here the reasons for any errors, stating clearly how the errors will be avoided in future.

Start date	**End date**	**Time taken (hours)**	**Signed satisfactory by supervisor**

| **Exercise 3.8** | *Basic centre lathe turning test* |

The multiple choice question paper will only be issued to candidates by their supervisor on satisfactory completion of the appropriate exercises. The answer sheet below must be completed by the candidate when the questions are issued.

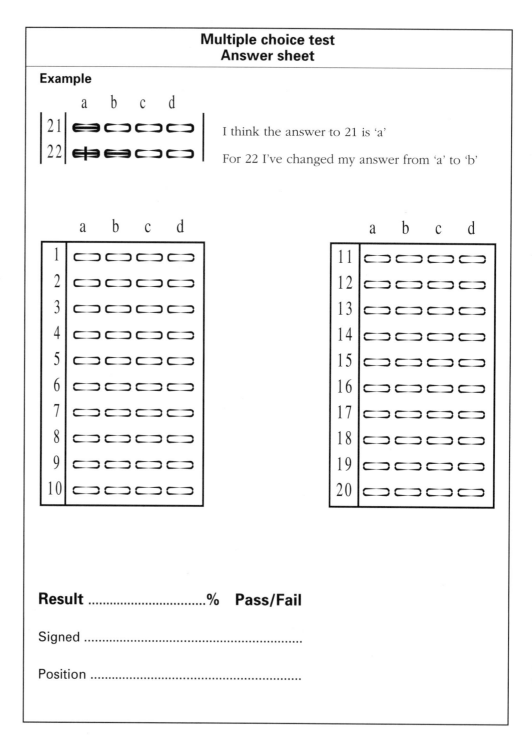

**Multiple choice test
Answer sheet**

Example

```
     a   b   c   d
21 [==] [=] [=] [=]    I think the answer to 21 is 'a'

22 [==][==] [=] [=]    For 22 I've changed my answer from 'a' to 'b'
```

Result ....% **Pass/Fail**

Signed ....

Position ....

Chapter 4
Basic milling

Exercise		Page	Date	Signed by Trainer
4.1	Stepped block (vertical milling)	120		
4.2	Slotted clamp (vertical milling)	127		
4.3	Milling fixture (horizontal milling)			
4.4	Tee			
4.5	Turni verti			
4.6	Multi			
The trainee procedures				
The trainee h clothing				
The trainee h tidy				
The trainee h ... observe Health & Safety requirements and observes good working practices				

Milling is the machining process generally selected for producing rectangular and angular workpieces with plane flat surfaces. Drilled and bored holes can also be accurately positioned with a milling machine. Milling involves feeding a securely held workpiece past a revolving multi-tooth cutting tool called a milling cutter. The sharp edges of the milling cutter remove material from the workpiece. The shape of the finished workpiece depends on:

- the movement of the workpiece relative to the cutter
- the shape of the cutter.

The operator of a milling machine is called a miller.

The column and knee design of milling machines are generally used for producing small quantities of components. Column and knee milling machines are available with either:

- a vertical spindle, called a vertical milling machine

  or
- a horizontal spindle, called a horizontal milling machine.

Vertical and horizontal milling machines have a similar lower construction, a solid 'column' and an adjustable 'knee'. Both types of machine are used to produce rectangular and angular workpieces with plane flat surfaces and holes can also be drilled, bored and tapped. Vertical milling machines are more versatile and better suited to drilling whilst horizontal milling machines are more often used for heavy duty work and production.

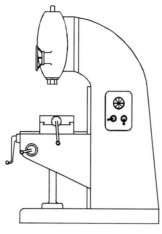
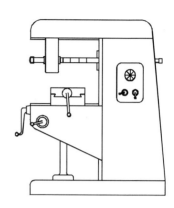

Vertical milling machine   Horizontal milling machine

The principle differences between vertical and horizontal milling machines are:

- the cutting tool is held in a different plane, depending on whether the machine has a vertical or a horizontal spindle
- different cutting tools are used
- the cutting tools are held in a different way.

For the exercises in this chapter you will use both a vertical and a horizontal milling machine.

We start by examining the common types of vertical milling machine.

The vertical milling machine

There are two different types of vertical milling machines shown below. Both have a main frame called a column, and a work table mounted on a knee which adjusts the table's height (known as knee and column vertical milling machine).

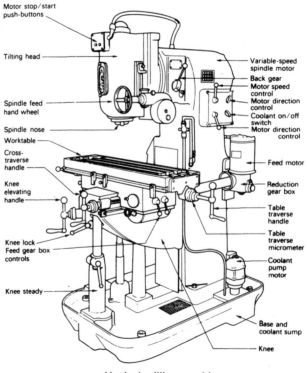

Vertical milling machine

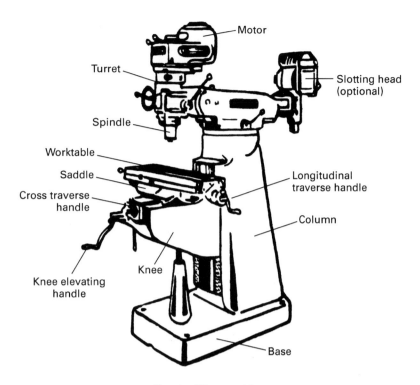

Turret milling machine

The workpiece is securely held onto the machine's table in a work-holding device, usually a vice or special fixture. The cutting tool is fixed in the machine's spindle and rotated. The workpiece is traversed relative to the tool, thus removing material.

The fundamental parts of vertical milling machines are labelled on the above diagrams:

1. **The spindle**

   The spindle is the rotating part of the machine, it houses the chuck and cutting tool. The spindle's axis is vertical on all vertical milling machines. The spindle's bore is finely finished to a standard taper size so that standard tool holding devices, i.e. chucks, can be mounted. The spindle's speed can be set with levers and pulley belts to give a range of speeds.

2. **The column**

   The main frame of all milling machines is called the column. It must be rigid to withstand the cutting forces so it is usually substantial in size and made in a box section from cast iron. The column on standard vertical milling machines contains the main motor and gearboxes to provide a range of speeds for table movement (feeds).

   At the foot of the column is a hollow base which provides a reservoir for the coolant and a platform for the machine to stand on.

3. **The turret (turret type only)**

   The head of the turret is mounted on a sliding beam and contains the spindle motor. The spindle can be raised or lowered with a lever in a similar way to a drilling machine. The turret head can be tilted both sideways and forward or backwards, this feature makes the machine very versatile but less rigid than the standard type vertical milling machine.

4. **The knee bracket**

   The knee supports the machine's saddle so that the table is level and at 90° to the spindle. The knee is a large slide mounted on vertical dovetail slides at the front of the column, it is raised and lowered by a handle which operates the jacking screw.

5. **The saddle**

   The saddle slides across the top surface of the knee bracket and has another slideway across its top surface to enable the machine's table to be fed longitudinally.

6. **The table**

The table is fed longitudinally or transversely and carries the workpiece past the revolving cutter. The table has a large accurately machined upper surface and tee slots used to mount the workpiece or work-holding device. The inside of the tee slots is machined to accurately locate work-holding devices via small pegs called tenons.

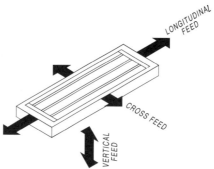

Table movements

7. **Vertical milling machine sizes**

The size of a vertical milling machine is measured in two ways:

(a) Table size.
(b) Traverse lengths.

The power of the motor would also be quoted in a machine specification.

Milling techniques used on vertical milling machines

Two basic techniques used to produce components on a vertical milling machine are shown below:

Milling with the face of the cutter

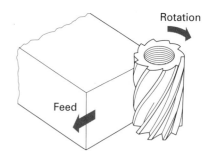

Milling with the side of the cutter

Work-holding using a vice

A vice is a simple and efficient method of securely holding workpieces of up to about 150 mm long on a milling machine's table. Machine vices may have two pegs fitted on the underside called tenons.

Tenons locate the vice into one of the machine's tee slots so the vice jaws are square to the machine's table. Vices with tenons can be set up quickly and accurately on the machine table. If tenons are not fitted to a vice, it must be set square accurately using a DTI (dial test indicator).

Three types of machine vices are shown below.

The plain machine vice

This is used for holding workpieces square to the machine's table. Plain machine vices are strong and rigid, when fitted with tenons they are quick to set up. A plain machine vice can be fitted to a swivel base which converts it into a swivelling machine vice.

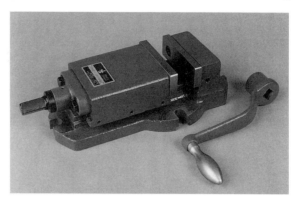

Plain machine vice

The swivelling machine vice

This is used for holding workpieces to the machine's table when machining angular workpieces. The angle is set by swivelling the body of the vice. The angle of the vice can be read off a rotary scale which is calibrated in degrees. The vice is then locked into position.

For swivelling vices to be accurately used they must be fitted with tenons which locate the vice on the machine's table so that when the vice is set at 0° the jaws hold the workpiece square to the table. If no tenons are fitted the vice must be set up as described below.

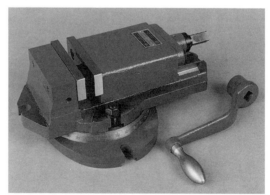

Swivel machine vice

Tilting and swivelling machine vice

Used when machining compound angles, the workpiece can be turned around at an angle and tilted upwards as shown. This type of vice is used for complicated jobs because it needs to be set both horizontal and square before starting work. This type of vice is less rigid than those above and can be time-consuming to accurately set up with a dial test indicator.

Tilting and swivelling machine vice

Pull-down vice jaws

These jaws can be fitted to any of the above machine vices. They effectively pull the workpiece down onto the vice base or packing, eliminating the need to tap the workpiece down after tightening the vice. Pull-down vice jaws may have plain or serrated faces.

Pull-down vice jaws

Safety note!
Always use the correct lifting technique when lifting heavy machine vices. This means bending at the knees and keeping your head up, so that your spine is vertical.

Always ask for help or use powered lifting equipment with loads that are too heavy or bulky for you to lift by yourself.

Make sure the machine has been isolated from the electrical supply before mounting or removing vices or fixtures.

Setting a vice square in a milling machine's table

When milling square faces on a workpiece, it is essential that the vice is mounted square on the machine's table. A machine vice fitted with tenons will always locate in this way but a vice without tenons should *always* be set square before any metal cutting can start. Setting the vice square can be carried out with a dial test indicator (DTI) mounted on a magnetic base.

After isolating the electrical supply, the procedure is as follows:

(a) Thoroughly clean the top of the machine table and the underside of the vice.

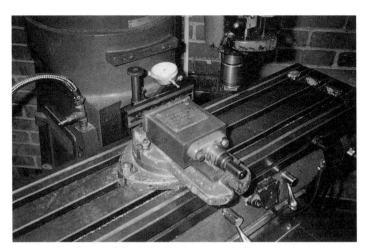

Setting a vice square with a DTI

(b) Lightly secure the machine vice to the machine table with two forged tee bolts, nuts and washers.
(c) If using a swivel vice, carefully set it at 0°.
(d) Hold a parallel bar in the vice jaws as shown.
(e) Mount a DTI on a magnetic base.
(f) Attach the magnetic base securely to the machine's column so that the DTI's anvil rests against one end of the parallel bar.
(g) Wind the table lengthways so that the DTI's pointer shows any out-of-parallel reading, note this reading.
(h) Tap the vice body to compensate for any out-of-parallel DTI reading.
(i) Tighten both of the vice's securing nuts.
(j) Finally check the vice in its fixed position for parallel. The DTI should have less than 0·05 mm TIR (total indicator reading).

Mounting workpieces in a vice

(a) When the machine vice is set square to the machine table the workpiece can be clamped in the machine vice. The predominant direction of the cutting force should always be towards the **fixed jaw** of the vice (as opposed to the moving jaw).

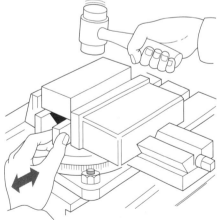

Workpiece mounted on parallel bars in a vice

(b) The workpiece is then mounted on a pair of parallel bars and the vice securely tightened with the handle.
(c) Tap the workpiece down with a hide hammer until both parallels are trapped tightly between the top of the vice and the workpiece. You now know that the underside of the workpiece is parallel to the top of the vice.

After being secured, the workpiece is slowly fed under a rotating milling cutter. The cutter should be carefully selected for the particular job in hand.

Selection of milling cutters for vertical milling

When selecting a milling cutter for vertical milling operations, choose a milling cutter which has the largest possible diameter. This is to maintain the cutter's rigidity.

The most common types of vertical milling cutter are described below.

End mill

Made from high-speed steel, these cutters are designed for profile milling. They can also be used for producing open slots. Close tolerance slots can only be produced with a small diameter cutter and opening up to size by further cuts.

Slot drill

Made from high speed steel, these cutters can be used to produce slots and keyways accurately to size. They are centre cutting and can plunge feed vertically into a workpiece to produce closed slots or pockets as one tooth extends to the centre of the tool.

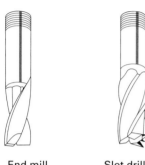

End mill   Slot drill

Other specially shaped high-speed steel cutters for vertical milling:

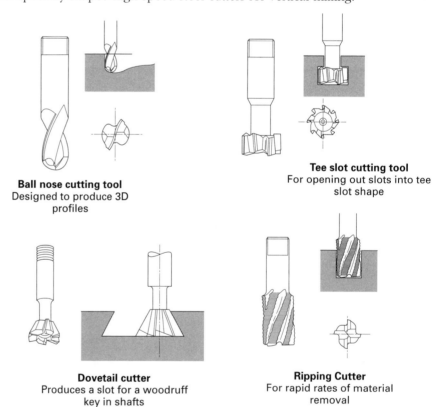

Ball nose cutting tool
Designed to produce 3D profiles

Tee slot cutting tool
For opening out slots into tee slot shape

Dovetail cutter
Produces a slot for a woodruff key in shafts

Ripping Cutter
For rapid rates of material removal

Large diameter cutters for vertical milling are described below.

Shell end mill

Large cutter used for facing large flat surfaces. Shell end mills are mounted on a tool-holding device called a stub arbor. The high-speed steel cutting shell is fixed onto the stub arbor with a screw. Positive drive is ensured by two slots in the shell locating with driving dogs on the stub arbor.

Face mills

Face mills fit directly into stub arbors fitted in the machine's spindle, this gives maximum rigidity. They are fitted with indexable high-speed steel or tungsten carbide inserts which makes them very hard. Although this type of cutter is very expensive, the hard and rigid combination enables faster cutting speeds to be used for more rapid production rates.

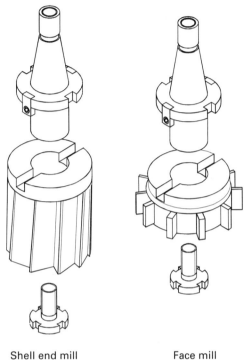

Shell end mill   Face mill

Mounting a chuck in a vertical milling machine

Chucks are the most common cutting tool-holding device used for vertical milling operations. Before you mount the cutting tool, you must fit a chuck in the spindle correctly.

The procedure is as follows:

(a) Clean the inside of the machine's spindle and the tapered end of the chuck with a clean cloth.
(b) Reach up to the top of the machine's spindle and hold the drawbar.
(c) Locate the chuck in the driving lugs on the spindle nose.
(d) Insert the chuck's taper into the spindle's tapered hole.
(e) Screw the drawbar into the end of the chuck and tighten with the locknut.

Mounting the cutter in a vertical milling machine

Milling cutters are sharp and should be handled with leather gloves.

> **Safety** – *always isolate the machine before changing the milling cutter; should the machine be accidentally started a serious accident could result.*

The usual chuck used on a vertical milling machine for holding end mills and slot drills is similar to the Dormer fastloc chuck shown below. This type of chuck is designed to hold screwed shank cutters efficiently.

The chuck incorporates all the advantages of the self-locking technique for screwed shank cutters: a hardened and ground centre and a screwed precision collet which is free to rotate with the locking nut for automatic tightening under heavy cuts.

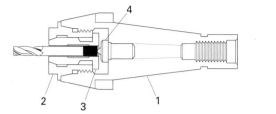

Component parts
1 Fastloc chuck body
2 Locking nut
3 Collet
4 Centre pin

The internal locking nut has a precision ground taper location with the chuck body to maintain concentricity even after years of use.

Assembly instructions for mounting end mills or slot drills in a milling chuck

(a) All component parts must be clean before assembly, particulary the ground taper locations.
(b) The collet should be inserted into the locking nut, making sure that the driving flats are engaged in the locking nut flats.
(c) The collet and locking nut assembly should then be inserted into the chuck body and screwed in until the mating tapers of the locking nut and the chuck body are engaged.
(d) The selected cutter should then be inserted into the collet and screwed in by hand pressure, until it firmly locates on the centre pin. Wear protective gloves for this operation.
(e) Tighten the locking nut with the special spanner, ensuring that the mating tapers are securely located.

To release the cutter
Using the ring spanner provided, release the locking nut slightly until the cutter can be unscrewed from the collet by hand.

Selection of spindle speeds for milling

The correct speed to set the machine spindle, and hence the cutter, depends upon four factors:

* The diameter of the cutter
* The type of material being cut
* The material from which the cutting tool is made
* The availability of coolant

To calculate the correct speed with the correct cutting fluid, use the formula:

$$\text{Rev}/\min = \frac{1000 \times S}{\pi \times d}$$

Where S = Cutting speed of the work material
d = Cutting tool diameter
π = 3·142 (often approximated to 3)

See Appendix VII for the cutting speeds for various tool/workpiece combinations to use as a guide. Some cutting tool manufacturers recommend different speeds to those quoted in Appendix VII.

Selecting feed rate

The feed rate for milling cutters should be carefully selected. Feed rates for milling are usually stated as mm per minute. The feed rate depends on the spindle speed, the number of teeth on the cutter and the feed per cutter tooth. The correct feed rate for a milling operation can be calculated by referring to Appendix VIII to find the recommended feed rate per tooth and using the formula:

Feed per minute = Rev/min × No of teeth on cutter × recommended feed/tooth

Direction of feed

The two views shown below are alternative methods of removing material with the side of a milling cutter. Although both methods are practical in theory, up-cut milling should normally be used.

Study the up-cut milling drawing carefully. Note that the direction of the cutting tool's point is in the opposite direction to which the workpiece is being fed. The chip starts to be cut at point A and parted from the workpiece at point B, i.e. the chip formation starts thin and ends thick.

When using the up-cut milling technique the opposing directions of movement of tool and work prevent the cutter snatching the work in if there is any slack between the leadscrew and its driving nut.

The down-cut milling method (sometimes called climb milling) will give a better surface finish because the chip starts thick at point C and finishes thin at point D. Down-cut milling can be used for heavier cuts because each tooth passing the workpiece pushes the workpiece down onto the parallels.

Although down-cut milling offers these advantages, it should *not* to be used on general tool room milling machines.

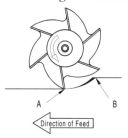

A   B

Direction of Feed

Up-cut milling –
recommended for most
conventional operations

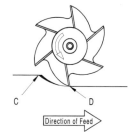

C   D

Direction of Feed

Down-cut milling – only for
special machines

Positioning of guards

Milling is an extremely dangerous process.

Safety - never touch a rotating cutter or attempt to clear away swarf while the machine is running. It is essential that all machine guards are positioned and used appropriately to offer maximum protection for you, the operator.

For vertical milling machines the enclosure mill guard is typical. The guard is transparent and in the closed position protects the operator from flying debris and being splashed by coolant. More importantly the guard prevents the operator becoming entangled with any moving parts.

When opened this type of guard offers unrestricted access to the machine's table and work area. Guards of this type are very efficient as they are easy to fit, guard the whole of the cutting area and are transparent.

Electrical interlocks are sometimes fitted with this type of guard to prevent the machine from being started until the guard has been positioned and locked into place.

The Health and Safety at Work Act 1974 states that you must take reasonable care of the health and safety of yourself and other persons who may be affected by your acts. This means you must *always* use guards and report any problems such as failure to operate properly, damage to guards or missing guards to your supervisor.

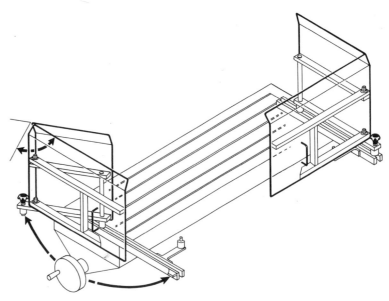

Enclosure mill guard opened for tool and work setting

Operating the vertical milling machine

*Safety – never work on any machine until you have been
shown how to operate it properly by a suitably qualified person.*

Your supervisor will arrange for you to be shown how to operate a vertical milling machine, and introduce you to the machine's features including:

- power supply, and how to isolate the machine when changing cutting tools and cleaning it
- guards and guarding systems to be used when operating the machine
- spindle stop, start and reverse controls
- handwheels and feed dials for longitudinal, vertical and cross feed
- spindle speed selection levers
- feed selection levers. feed engagement levers and trips for 'over travel'
- power feed control for traversing the work
- rapid feed (if available)
- locks on all three slides
- coolant/cutting fluid supply
- emergency stop procedure

*If you do not understand what you have been shown or
if you are unsure how to proceed you must **ask!***

*Safety – never operate a machine until the slideways are cleared of all tools and
equipment.*

When you have practised working the vertical milling machine using pieces of spare material, and have become confident with the controls, ask your supervisor for permission to start Exercise 4.1, Stepped block.

Exercise 4.1 | *Stepped block*

Make the stepped block using a vertical milling machine. Use the procedure and tools indicated. Your finished workpiece should be within the drawing limits.

On completion of the task, carefully measure your work and write in the table the actual sizes, noting any errors.

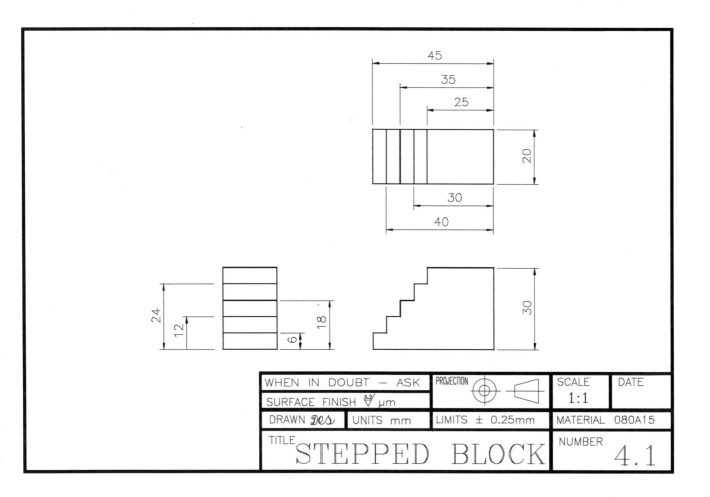

WHEN IN DOUBT — ASK
SURFACE FINISH ∇ 3.2 μm
DRAWN *Des* UNITS mm
PROJECTION
SCALE 1:1 DATE
LIMITS ± 0.25mm MATERIAL 080A15
TITLE STEPPED BLOCK NUMBER 4.1

Planning

Procedure
1 Acquire material, check for size, and de-burr all sharp edges.
2 Hold work in a plain machine vice on parallel bars
3 Mount end mill in chuck, set spindle speed and feed rate
4 Machine ends square and to length
5 Mark out guidelines on workpiece blank
6 Set up workpiece vertically in vice
7 Touch on workpiece top and side, setting registers at zero
8 Machine all steps on workpiece
9 De-burr all sharp edges
10 Stamp your name on your work
11 Isolate machine from the electricity supply
12 Clean the work area and machine

Tools and equipment selected
Vertical milling machine
End mill
Collet chuck
Machine vice & parallel bars
Hide hammer
Metric 300 mm rule
0 – 25 mm micrometer
25 – 50 mm micrometer
Letter stamps

Examine a **vertical milling machine** and complete the tables with the following information.

Make of machine	
Model of machine	
Type of vertical milling machine (standard or turret).	
Maximum longitudinal traverse	
Cutting tool holding device	
Maximum traverse length of the spindle (if appropriate)	
One graduation on the longitudinal slide reduces the work's size by	
One graduation on the cross slide reduces the work's size by	
Number of spindle speeds available on the machine	
The position of the automatic feed engagement lever.	
Correct spindle speed for mild steel using a ø25 HSS end mill.	
Correct feed rate mild steel using a ø25 mm 4-tooth HSS end mill.	

Write here the **emergency stop procedure** for the vertical milling machine.

1

2

3

Write here why it is important to isolate the machine before changing cutting tools and before cleaning the machine.

1

2

Sketch

Make a sketch to show how the concentricity of the cutter can be checked using a dial test indicator.

Finished inspection report

Component dimensions (mm)	Limits	Actual size	Error
Length 45	45.25 44.75		
Length 35	35.25 34.75		
Length 25	25.25 24.75		
Height 18	18.25 17.75		
Height 24	24.25 23.75		
Remarks			

Results

Is the workpiece to the drawing specification?

Yes	No

If the completed workpiece is below drawing specification, write here the reasons for any errors, stating clearly how the errors will be avoided in future.

Start date	End date	Time taken (hours)	Signed satisfactory by supervisor

Cutting angular faces

When angles are specified on a drawing, the workpiece can be set up in a vice at the required angle and then fed under the cutter. A quick and reliable method of setting up angular workpieces for machining is either:

1. in a rigid machine vice, with the workpiece *inclined* at the required angle
   or
2. in a swivel machine vice, with the workpiece *turned* to the required angle.

Setting a workpiece in a rigid machine vice inclined at an angle

The procedure is as follows:

(a) Isolate the machine's electrical supply.
(b) Select a rigid machine vice with tenons which fit the table's tee slots.
(c) Thoroughly clean the top surface of the milling machine table and the bottom surface of the machine vice.
(d) Clamp the vice securely to the machine table.
(e) Check the vice is fitted square.
(f) Mark out the workpiece.

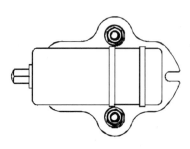

A rigid machine vice

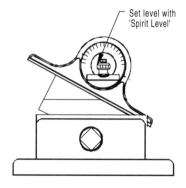

Set level with 'Spirit Level'

Workpiece set at 27° in a rigid machine vice

(g) Clamp the workpiece between the vice's jaws.
(h) Adjust a combination set's protractor head at the required angle (e.g. 27°).
(i) Rest the protractor against the workpiece and tilt the workpiece until the spirit level indicates level.
(j) Tighten the workpiece securely in the vice.
(k) Mount all machine guards.

Setting a workpiece in a swivelling vice turned at the required angle

The procedure is as follows:

(a) Isolate the machine's electrical supply.
(b) Select a swivel type machine vice with tenons which fit the table's tee slots.
(c) Thoroughly clean the top surface of the milling machine table and the bottom surface of the machine vice.
(d) Clamp the vice securely to the machine table.
(e) Slacken the locking nuts on the swivel base of the vice and turn the vice through the required angle (e.g. 63°).
(f) Lock the vice at the required angular setting.
(g) Check the angle is correct.
(h) Tap the workpiece down tight onto the parallel bars with a hide hammer.
(i) Make sure the parallel bars will not interfere with the cutting process.
(j) Make sure there is room for the cutter to clear the workpiece after it has cut the material.
(k) Mount all machine guards.

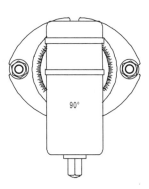

A swivel type machine vice

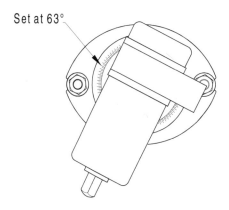

Set at 63°

Workpiece set at 63° in a swivel vice

Machining angular workpieces

(a) Mark out the finished angle on the workpiece and mount the workpiece in a machine vice as outlined above.
(b) Fit the chuck in the machine spindle, and mount an end mill.
(c) Select and set the correct spindle speed and feed rate.
(d) Position the machine table so that the side of the cutter is ready to cut the material using up-cut milling.
(e) Mount **all** guards.
(f) Turn on the electrical supply.
(g) Machine the surface using appropriate coolant.
(h) On completion of the machining process, isolate the machine and carefully remove the workpiece.

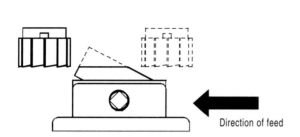

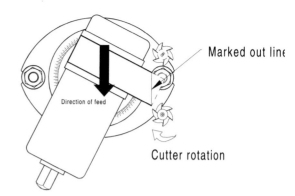

Marked out line

Direction of feed

Cutter rotation

Milling angular workpieces in a rigid vice

Direction of feed

Milling angular workpieces in a swivel vice

Slot drilling

Slot drilling is the process of cutting closed slots into workpieces. To make such shapes a slot drill must be used because it has a cutting edge extending to the tool's centre allowing it to be fed vertically down into the workpiece.

(a) Mark out guidelines on the workpiece.
(b) Mount the work-holding device square on the milling machine's table.
(c) Fit a slot drill which has a diameter smaller than the width of the required slot. The smaller cutter allows the slot to be accurately opened out to width.
(d) Set the machine's spindle speed and feed rate appropriately.
(e) Position the table so that the milling cutter is near the side of the workpiece. Carefully move the table until the cutter *just* touches the side of the workpiece (Figure 1).
(f) Set the table's handwheel reading to zero.
(g) Lower the table so that the end of the milling cutter is clear of the workpiece.
(h) Move the table sideways one half of the cutter's diameter so that the centre of the cutter is in line with the edge of the workpiece (Figure 2).
(i) Reset the table's handwheel reading to zero.
(j) Now you can wind the table sideways the appropriate distance on the drawing so that the cutter's axis is exactly above the slot centre line.
(k) Position the guards and turn on the machine.
(l) Slowly plunge the cutter downwards into the workpiece to a maximum depth equal to the cutter's diameter (Figure 3).
(m) Feed the workpiece sideways to cut the slot the correct length.
(n) Repeat stage (l)–(m) by applying cuts by plunging the cutter slowly into the workpiece and feeding along the length of the slot until the full depth is reached.
(o) Measure the width of the sides of the workpiece. Wind the table sideways to open out the slot if necessary to correct any positional error. Remember to up-cut mill when doing this.

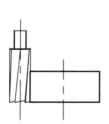

Figure 1
Touching the side of the workpiece

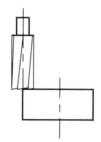

Figure 2
Centre of cutter in line with edge of workpiece

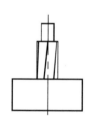

Figure 3
Cutting a slot with a slot drill

Exercise 4.2 · *Slotted clamp*

Make the slotted clamp using a vertical milling machine. Use the procedure and tools indicated. Your finished workpiece should be within the drawing limits. Carefully measure your work and write in the table the actual sizes, noting any errors.

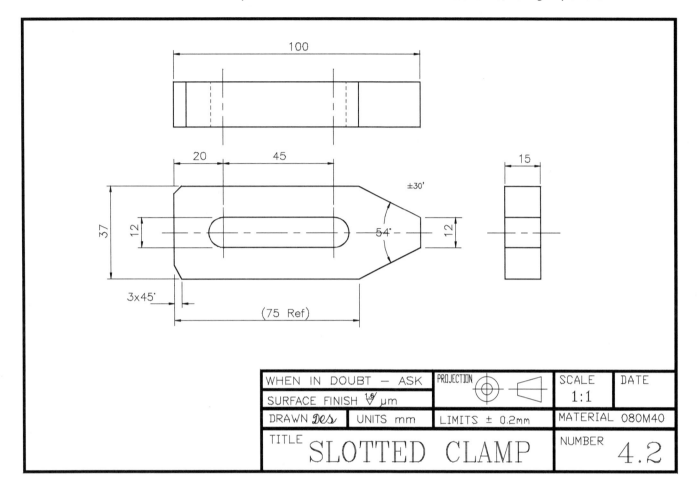

WHEN IN DOUBT — ASK	PROJECTION	SCALE 1:1	DATE
SURFACE FINISH ¹·⁶∕ μm			
DRAWN 𝒟𝒪𝒮	UNITS mm	LIMITS ± 0.2mm	MATERIAL 080M40
TITLE SLOTTED CLAMP		NUMBER 4.2	

Planning

Procedure	Tools and equipment selected
1 Acquire material and check for size	Vertical milling machine
2 Mount the vice on the machine and set square	End mill
3 Set the workpiece on the vice using parallel bars	Slot drill
4 Mount the end mill and set speed and feed	Collet chuck
5 Machine blank to size	Machine vice & parallel bars
6 Mark out guidelines on workpiece	Hide hammer
7 Mount workpiece at 27° and machine each angle, reset workpiece at 45° and machine the corner chamfers	300 mm rule
	0–25 mm micrometer
8 Change the cutter for the slot drill	25–50 mm micrometer
9 Machine the slot in position	Vernier calliper
10 Isolate machine from the electrical supply	Letter stamps
11 De-burr all sharp edges and stamp your name on work	
12 Clean the work area and the machine	

Complete the tables with correct information.

List all the machine guards available on your machine	
Spindle speed used for (a) end mill	
(b) slot drill	
Feed rate selected for (a) end mill	
(b) slot drill	

Write here how you checked the vice was secure on the machine table.

1

2

3

Write here how you ensured the workpiece was securely held in the vice.

1

2

Sketch

Make a sketch of the cutting process and indicate clearly:

1   Vice securing arrangement
2   Up-cut milling
3   Workpiece seated on parallels
4   Cutter's thrust is towards the fixed jaw of the vice

Finished inspection report

Component dimensions (mm)	Limits	Actual size	Error
Body width 37	37·2 36·8		
Slot width 12	12·2 11·8		
Slot length 57	57·2 56·8		
Overall length 100	100·2 99·8		
Angle 54°	54°30' 53°30'		
Remarks			

Results

Is the workpiece to the drawing specification?

Yes		No

If the completed workpiece is below drawing specification, write here the reasons for any errors, stating clearly how the errors will be avoided in future.

Start date	End date	Time taken (hours)	Signed satisfactory by supervisor

Horizontal milling machines

The two principle differences between vertical and horizontal milling machines are the orientation of the machine's spindle and the type of cutting tools used.

There are two types of horizontal milling machine:

- Plain horizontal milling machine
- Universal milling machine which has a swivelling table

Knee and column horizontal milling machines

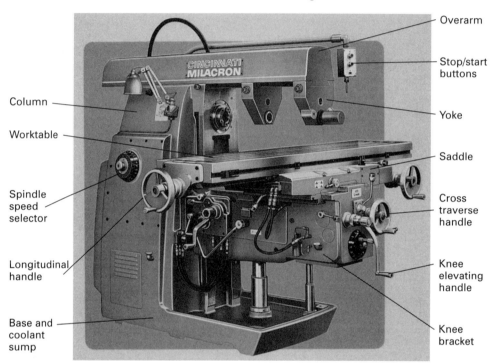

Column —

Worktable —

Spindle speed selector —

Longitudinal handle —

Base and coolant sump —

— Overarm

— Stop/start buttons

— Yoke

— Saddle

— Cross traverse handle

— Knee elevating handle

— Knee bracket

Plain horizontal milling machine

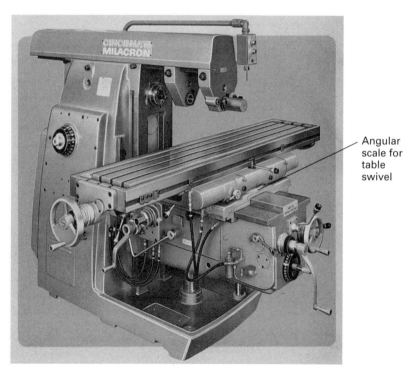

— Angular scale for table swivel

Universal milling machine

Horizontal milling machines are very rigid and robust; they are used to produce rectangular and angular workpieces with plane flat surfaces. The plain horizontal milling machine is a less versatile machine than the vertical milling machine. On a horizontal milling machine, a multi-tooth cutting tool is fixed onto the standard tool-holding device called the arbor. The arbor is a long shaft fitted into the spindle of the machine by a taper; it is supported by a yoke.

As with vertical milling, the workpiece is securely held in a work-holding device which is usually a machine vice or a special fixture. The workpiece is fed relative to the rotating cutting tool, thus removing material.

The swivelling table on the universal milling machine enables the machine to be used for machining complex shapes and angles using various attachments.

The horizontal milling machine is to be used for the next two exercises in this work book.

The fundamental parts of a horizontal milling machine are labelled on the above diagrams and described below.

1. **The spindle**

   The rotating part of the machine into which the arbor and cutting tool is mounted. Its bore is finely finished to a standard taper size so that the arbor can be mounted. The spindle's speed can be set with levers and pulley belts.

   Note that the spindle is in a horizontal plane on the horizontal milling machine.

2. **The column**

   The frame of the machine must be rigid to withstand the cutting forces. The column contains the main motor and gearboxes to provide a range of speeds for table movement (feeds). The machines shown above are rigid production machines.

   At the foot of the column is a base which provides a reservoir for the coolant and a platform for the machine to stand on.

3. **Overarm**

   The overarm is a rail on the top of the machine. It has a guideway which houses one or sometimes two yokes. When setting up a machine you should always have the overarm retracted back as far as possible to reduce deflection of the arbor.

4. **Yoke**

   The yoke is mounted on the overarm and supports the arbor, reducing the chances of bending the arbor and providing rigidity and stability to the cutting tool.

5. **The knee bracket**

   The knee supports the machine's saddle so that the table is level and at 90° to the spindle. The knee is a large slide mounted on vertical dovetail slides at the front of the column, it is raised and lowered by a handle which operates the jacking screw.

6. **The saddle**

   The saddle slides transversely along the top surface of the knee bracket. It has slideways across its top surface to enable the machine's table to be fed longitudinally. The saddle on universal milling machines is split in the middle to allow the table to be swivelled at an angle.

7. **The table**

   The table has a large accurately machined horizontal upper surface which is used to mount the work-holding device or workpiece. A series of accurately machined tee slots are used for clamping. The inside of these tee slots is machined to accurately locate workholding devices via tenons fitted to the underside of vices, etc.

   The table is fed longitudinally or transversely and carries the workpiece past the revolving cutter.

8. **Horizontal milling machine sizes**

   The size of a milling machine is measured in two ways:

   (a) Table size
   (b) Traverse lengths (i.e. the maximum movements the table can be traversed)

   The power of the motor is also quoted in the machine's specification.

Basic techniques used to produce components on a horizontal milling machine are shown below:

Basic horizontal milling operations

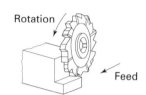

Milling with side of cutter

Milling with face of cutter

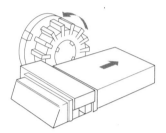

Milling with cutter mounted
in chuck or stub arbor

Note: vertical milling machines are preferred for drilling holes because the operator has a better view of the workpiece.

Work-holding in a horizontal milling machine

When setting up a workpiece in a horizontal milling machine, the workpiece should be mounted in a work-holding device in the same way as it would be for a vertical milling machine. For information on setting and selecting vices, see pages 112–16.

Selection of cutters for horizontal milling

There is a greater choice of cutters for horizontal milling than vertical milling. The cutter rotates and removes material as the workpiece traverses past it. There are three basic types of cutter, most are made out of high-speed steel, although carbide tipped tooling is used on some types of tool.

- Plain milling cutters
- Form relieved cutters
- Chuck and stub arbor-mounted cutters

Plain milling cutters

1. **Slab mill** (cylindrical cutters):
   Used for cutting on its outside edge only (the periphery), slab mills are used for machining wide flat surfaces. Helical (spiral) teeth cutters have the advantage of more than one tooth cutting at a time, this reduces chatter and vibration.
2. **Side and face cutter**
   This has teeth on both sides and on its periphery. It is used to machine the face of workpieces and to take vertical cuts.
   It is normally made from high-speed steel, although side and face cutters are also available with inserted carbide or high-speed steel tips.
   It is not used for cutting slots in one pass as vibrations cause the sides of the cutter to cut the slot over-size.

3. **Slotting cutter**

    Available in set sizes, slotting cutters are used to cut slots accurately to a specified width in one pass. They have teeth on their periphery but not on their sides. The width of a slot cut with a slotting cutter is the same as the width of the cutter.

4. **Slitting saw**

    This type of cutter is used to cut material to length and to cut narrow slots of between 1 mm and 5 mm wide through a workpiece. Slitting saws are large diameter cutters (200 mm is typical), and only have teeth on their periphery.

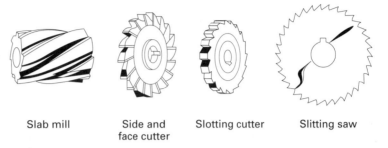

| Slab mill | Side and face cutter | Slotting cutter | Slitting saw |

Form relieved cutters

1. **Single angle cutter**

    This has a specified angle on one face. The angle on this type of cutter enables the machining of angular faces and chamfers on corners. When using angle cutters, avoid heavy loads on the points of the cutting edges as they are easily chipped.

2. **Double angle cutter**

    This has specific angles on both faces and is often used for machining such items as splines and milling cutters.

3. **Convex cutter**

    This is used to machine rounded slots and grooves in the surface of workpieces. 'Convex' refers to the shape of the cutter.

4. **Radius (corner rounding) cutter**

    For finishing off corners on large workpieces. A different cutter is required for each radius so this is only used to finish off components when large quantities are required.

    Radius cutters are also available with a full radius for rounding the ends of workpieces.

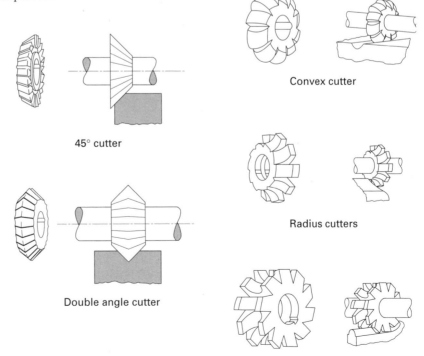

45° cutter

Convex cutter

Double angle cutter

Radius cutters

Full radius concave cutter

Chuck and stub arbor-mounted cutters

These cutters are the same as those used in vertical milling. They are mounted in exactly the same way (see page 117).

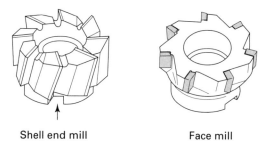

Shell end mill   Face mill

Fitting arbor-mounted cutters in a horizontal milling machine

Horizontal milling cutters are mounted on the machine's arbor. The position of the cutter is adjusted by selecting and positioning spacing collars on either side of the cutter. It is advisable to mount the cutter as close as reasonably possible to the machine's column to maintain rigidity. The yoke is used to support the arbor and runs on a larger collar which acts as a bearing.

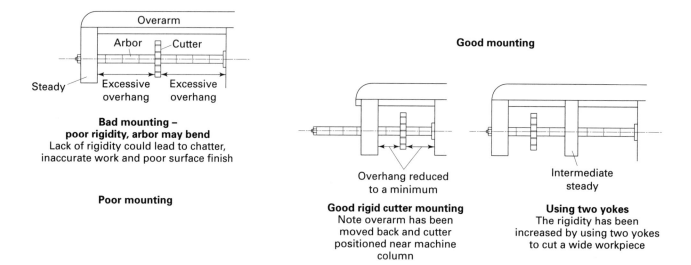

Good mounting

Overarm

Arbor — Cutter

Steady

Excessive overhang   Excessive overhang

**Bad mounting –
poor rigidity, arbor may bend**
Lack of rigidity could lead to chatter,
inaccurate work and poor surface finish

Poor mounting

Overhang reduced
to a minimum

Intermediate
steady

Good rigid cutter mounting
Note overarm has been
moved back and cutter
positioned near machine
column

Using two yokes
The rigidity has been
increased by using two yokes
to cut a wide workpiece

Milling arbors are tool-holding devices and are manufactured from high tensile alloy steel for strength. They have an accurately finished parallel cylindrical surface and a tapered end which fits into the machine's spindle. Milling arbors are located in the spindle nose's driving pegs and taper, then secured in position with a draw bolt which screws into the end of the arbor.

Spacing collars are for positioning the cutter and are made from case hardened steel.

The length of spacing collars are made to standard sizes. The ends are parallel.

One collar, called a bearing bush has a larger diameter than the others. The bearing bush fits inside the yoke and steadies the arbor during cutting to prevent it bending.

A large nut is fitted to the end of the arbor to hold the collars, milling cutter and bearing bush in position. The nut may have either a left- or a right-hand thread.

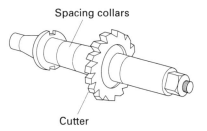

Spacing collars

Cutter

Milling arbor and spacing collars

Mounting arbors and cutters on a horizontal milling machine

The procedure is as follows:

(a) Clean the inside of the machine's spindle and the tapered end of the arbor with a clean cloth.
(b) Remove the yoke from the overarm.
(c) At the back of machine, insert the drawbar into the spindle.
(d) Insert the arbor's taper into the tapered hole of the spindle nose.
(e) Screw the drawbar into the end of the arbor and tighten with the locknut.

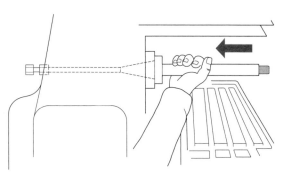

Mounting the arbor

(f) Clean the arbor's outer surface and the inside and sides of all spacing collars.
(g) Put spacing collars onto the arbor to locate the cutter.
(h) Fit a short key into the arbor's keyway.

> *Note:* (i) The key must *not* extend beyond the sides of the cutter.
> (ii) A key is not required for cutters under 6 mm thick.

(i) Select the direction of rotation of the cutter.

- The cutter should rotate in the *opposite* direction to the arbor's nut when the nut is being tightened (some arbors have left-hand threads).
- The cutter's rotation should be *against* the vice's fixed jaw or solid abutment of work-holding device.

(j) Mount the cutter close to the column end of the machine to maximise rigidity.

> **Safety** – *use gloves or cloth to protect your hands when handling milling cutters.*

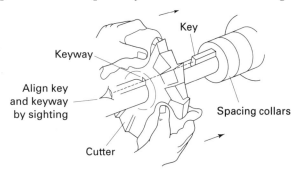

Key

Keyway

Align key
and keyway
by sighting

Spacing collars

Cutter

Mounting the cutter – note the short key

(k) Fit more spacing collars to position the cutter in a rigid position.
(l) Fit the bearing bush as close to the milling cutter as possible to lessen the chances of bending the arbor.
(m) Fit more spacing collars to 'fill' the arbor up to the thread on the end.
(n) Fit and tighten yoke in position.
(o) Tighten the nut on the end of the arbor.
(p) Mount the cutter guard.

Positioning guards

Horizontal milling is an extremely dangerous process. You must never touch a rotating cutter or attempt to clear away swarf while the machine is running, otherwise your hand may get caught in the cutter. It is essential that all machine guards are positioned and used appropriately to offer maximum protection for you, the operator.

The guard used for vertical milling is also suitable for horizontal milling machines but cutter guards are also frequently used.

A popular type of cutter guard for horizontal milling machines is shown. The guard is of all steel construction and can be quickly adjusted to fit around the milling cutter. It will protect the operator from flying debris and prevent him from becoming entangled with moving parts.

You must *always* use guards provided on machine tools. Report any problems such as failure to operate properly, damage to guards etc. to your supervisor. The requirements of The Health and Safety at Work Act 1974 require you to do so.

Cutter guard fitted to a horizontal milling machine

Exercise 4.3

Milling fixture

Make the milling fixture using a horizontal milling machine following the procedure and tools indicated. Your finished work should be within the drawing limits.

On completion of the task, carefully measure your work and write in the table the actual sizes, noting any errors.

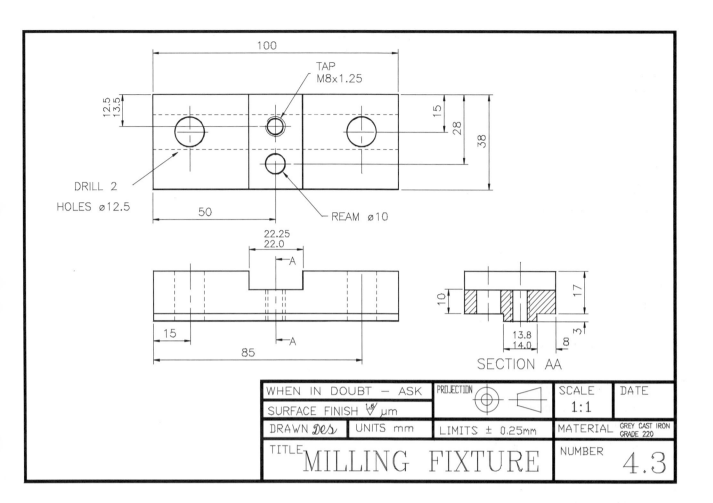

Planning

Procedure	Tools and equipment selected
1 Acquire material and check for size	Horizontal milling machine
2 Hold workpiece horizontally in a machine vice	Machine vice & parallel bars
3 Mount side and face cutter	Side & face milling cutter
4 Set spindle speed and feed rate	Slab mill
5 Machine ends square and to 100 mm long	Slotting cutter
6 Mount slab mill; machine billet to size (43 mm x 20 mm)	Hide hammer
7 Turn over and swivel vice through 90°	300 mm rule
8 Mark out slot and tenon on workpiece	0–25 mm micrometer
9 Machine tenon underneath	25–50 mm micrometer
10 Isolate your machine from the electricity supply	Vernier calliper
11 De-burr all sharp edges, stamp your name on your work	Letter stamps
12 Clean the work area and machine	

Examine a **horizontal milling machine** and complete the tables with the following information.

Make of machine	
Model of machine	
Type of horizontal milling machine (plain or universal)	
Maximum table longitudinal traverse	
Maximum table cross traverse	
Maximum distance from spindle centre line to table	
One graduation on the longitudinal slide reduces the work's size by	
One graduation on the cross slide reduces the work's size by	
Number of spindle speeds available on the machine	
The position of the automatic feed engagement lever	
Correct spindle speed for mild steel using a ⌀75 HSS slab mill.	
Correct feed rate for mild steel using a ⌀75 mm 12-tooth HSS side and face cutter	

Write here the **safety procedures** to be observed when cleaning milling machines.

1

2

3

Write here the daily maintenance procedures for the machine you have been using.

1

2

Sketch

Draw a sketch to show how a milling arbor can be checked for bend using a dial test indicator.

Finished inspection report

Component dimensions (mm)	Limits	Actual size	Error
Width 38	38.25 37.75		
Slot width 22	22.25 22.0		
Tenon width	13.8 14.0		
Body thickness 10	10.25 9.75		
Length 100	100.25 99.75		
Remarks			

Results

Is the workpiece to the drawing specification?

Yes   **No**

If the completed workpiece is below drawing specification, write here the reasons for any errors, stating clearly how the errors will be avoided in future.

Start date	End date	Time taken (hours)	Signed satisfactory by supervisor

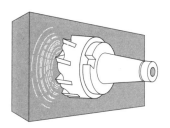

Stub arbor in a horizontal
milling machine

Stub arbor

A stub arbor can be fitted to the spindle nose of a horizontal milling machine. Stub arbors are used to hold shell end mills or face mills to machine large flat surfaces. Two principle advantages of using milling cutters in a stub arbor are:

- There is greater machine rigidity.
- The workpiece need not be reset between operations.

To fit a stub arbor or chuck in a horizontal milling machine

(a) Clean the inside of the machine's spindle and the tapered end of the stub arbor.
(b) Insert the stub arbor's taper into the spindle's tapered bore.
(c) Go to the back of the machine and insert the drawbar into the spindle.
(d) Screw the draw bolt into the end of the stub arbor and tighten with the locknut.
(e) Cutting tools are mounted in the same way as vertical milling machines (page 117).

Straddle milling

A workpiece can be milled on two surfaces at the same time if *two* side and face cutters are mounted on the arbor of a horizontal milling machine. The spacing collars are selected to give the required distance between the cutters. The procedure is called straddle milling. Straddle milling is used when a number of components are required with one feature the same size.

Setting up and straddle milling

(a) Select and mount a work holding device which will hold the workpiece with the faces to be milled exposed.
(b) Securely mount the workpiece (or a test piece) in the work-holding device – use solid fixed abutments where possible.
(c) Select a matched pair of side and face cutters and a range of spacing collars.
(d) Mount both side and face milling cutters on the machine's arbor separated by collars. The width of the collars should be equal to the required distance between the component's faces.
(e) Carefully measure the distance between the milling cutters' cutting edges. The distance can be adjusted by changing collars for ones with different widths or adding shims. Adjustable milling collars may also be used if available.
(f) Set the machine spindle speed and feed rate (Appendix VII).
(g) Position the machine's table so that the cutters cut the workpiece as required.
(h) Take a cut across part of the workpiece.
(i) Isolate the machine's electrical supply and measure the workpiece accurately and, if necessary, adjust the collar distance between the cutters on the arbor by either inserting, changing or removing milling collar shims.
(j) Re-cut the workpiece and, if necessary, repeat the above.

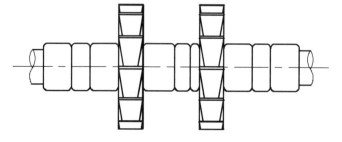

Pair of side and face cutters mounted ready for straddle milling

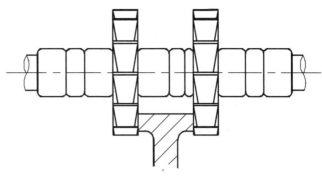

Straddle milling

Exercise 4.4 | *Tee nuts*

Make four tee nuts using a horizontal milling machine and your milling fixture (Exercise 4.3). Use the procedure and tools indicated. Your finished workpiece should be within the drawing limits.

On completion of the task, carefully measure your work and write in the table the actual sizes, noting any errors.

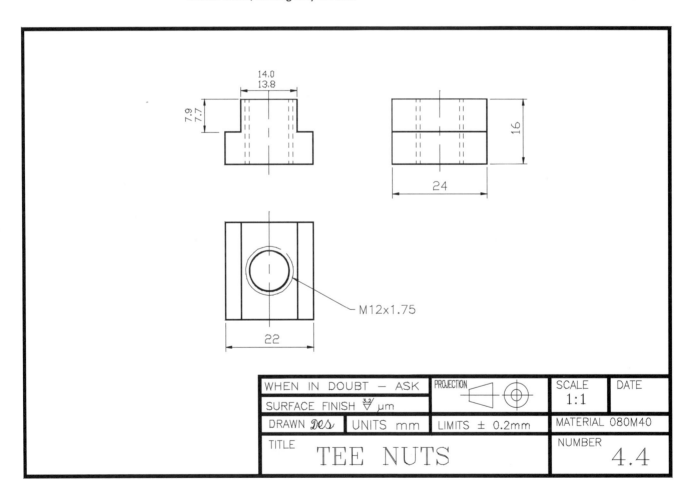

Planning

Procedure
1 Acquire material and check for size
2 Secure a vice on the machine's table
3 Hold workpiece horizontally in the milling fixture
4 Mount slab mill
5 Set spindle speed and feed rate
6 Machine top surface to size
7 Mount two side and face cutters
8 Machine 14 mm slot to width
9 Drill and tap M12 holes on a pillar drill
10 Mount a slitting saw, reset speed and feed
11 Mount the fixture square in the machine table
12 Cut off four pieces to length using the set up shown on page 147
13 Isolate your machine from the electricity supply
14 Clean the work area and machine
15 De-burr all sharp edges, stamp your name on your work

Tools and equipment selected
Horizontal milling machine
Milling fixture (Exercise 4.3)
Slab mill
Two side and face milling cutters
Slitting saw
Pillar drill
M12 taps
Tap wrench
300 mm rule
0–25 mm micrometer
Letter stamps

Complete the tables with correct information.

	Diameter	Width	No of teeth	Bore diameter
Accurate description of slab mill used to machine top of the billet				
Accurate description of the side and face cutter used for the slot				
Accurate description of the slitting saw used to cut tee nuts to length				

Write here the **safety procedures** to be observed when handling horizontal milling cutters.

1

2

3

Write here an accurate description of the machine arbor.

1 Overall length

3 Key width

2 Diameter

4 'Hand' of thread (left or right)

Sketch

Make a clear sketch of the cutter guard used on your horizontal milling machine.

Finished inspection report

Component dimensions (mm)	Limits	Actual size	Error
Tee width 14	14·0 13·8		
Overall height 16	16·2 15·8		
Step distance 8 (ref)	7·9 7·7		
Overall length 24	24·2 23·8		
Overall width 22	22·2 21·8		
Remarks			

Results

Is the workpiece to the drawing specification?

| Yes | | No |

> If the completed workpiece is below drawing specification, write here the reasons for any errors, stating clearly how the errors will be avoided in future.

Start date	End date	Time taken (hours)	Signed satisfactory by supervisor

Defects on milling cutters

Just like any other cutting tool, milling cutters suffer from wear and must be looked after to get the best performance. Looking after milling cutters means:

- Storing them individually so their teeth do not touch each other
- Using correct calculated spindle speeds
- Using correct feed rates for the material being cut
- Always using cutting fluid (except for cast iron)

Milling cutter storage rack

When a cutting tool is not producing a satisfactory surface finish, you should check the following before calling for assistance:

- Spindle speed is correct.
- Feed rate is correct.
- Coolant or cutting fluid is applied.

If the workpiece's surface finish is still poor after the above checks have been made, visually examine the actual cutting edges of the milling cutter, they may be:

Chipped

The milling cutters' points may be chipped due to the cutting edges being knocked against other cutting tools or hard objects.

To avoid damage to milling cutters in this way, milling cutters should be stored on a rack so that their cutting edges don't contact each other.

Worn

Milling cutter wear will always occur though it will be more rapid if:

- Spindle speeds are incorrectly set.
- Feedrates are incorrectly set.
- Coolant is not applied.

The above conditions will cause excessive heat to build up on the cutting tool's points which causes tiny thermal cracks to form, leading to tool point wear.

Built-up edge

Soft materials such as aluminium are prone to weld themselves to the top face of the cutting tool, this is called a built-up edge. A built-up edge can be avoided by:

- Polishing the front faces of the milling cutters surface
- Using milling cutters with greater rake angles
- Careful selection of coolant
- Using correct speed and feed rates

All worn tools should be reported and sharpened for best results. Many companies have set procedures for reporting defective cutting tools.

Chipped cutting edges   Worn flanks   Built-up edge

Other work-holding devices for use on milling machines

To continually achieve accuracy and a good surface finish it is essential that the workpiece is held securely. There are a variety of work-holding devices available to millers. Vices, as we have seen, are quick to set up and convenient to use, but they are not always the most appropriate work-holding method.

Other work-holding devices for use on milling machines are often required and the following factors should be considered when selecting a work-holding device.

1. **Workpiece shape**

   Irregular shaped workpieces cannot be held in ordinary vices, although special jaws may be specially made. Vee blocks held in the vice's jaws is a simple way to locate a cylindrical workpiece. If the workpiece being held is sand cast or has a particulary poor surface finish it would be more difficult to grip securely in a vice.

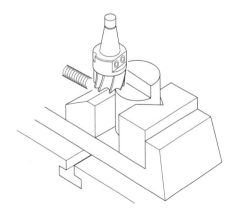

Cylindrical workpiece

2. **Workpiece size**

   Some workpieces cannot be held in vices because they are simply too big.

3. **Number of faces to be machined in one setting**

   A workpiece should be held so that the fewest number of set-ups are required. This is because setting up the machine is time-consuming and is a situation where errors can be made. Consequently, when choosing a work-holding device always make sure you can machine as many surfaces as possible.

4. **Quantity of workpieces to be machined**

   For batch production, workpieces must be changed quickly and successive components must locate in the machine in the same position as the last. This is especially important when using unskilled and semi-skilled labour.

   *Operator safety and workpiece security must always take priority over **all** other factors.*

   If a vice is unsuitable, one of the following work-holding devices can be selected depending on the workpiece to be machined:

Angle plate

The workpiece can be clamped to an angle plate when one surface is to be machined square to another on a large component. Angle plates with supporting ribs are best for milling operations as they are most rigid.

Bolt the angle plate to the machine table and then secure the workpiece on the angle plate.

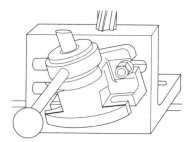

Using angle plate – note the teeth of the cutter force the workpiece
against the angle plate due to its direction of rotation

Clamped direct

Workpieces can be clamped directly to the machine table. This is often preferred when particulary large workpieces are to be machined.

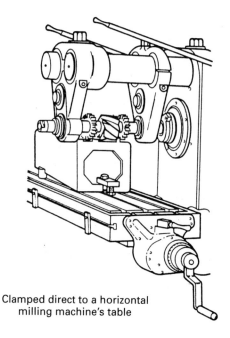

Clamped direct to a horizontal
milling machine's table

Vee blocks

Used to mount circular workpieces as shown to support a workpiece on a machine table.

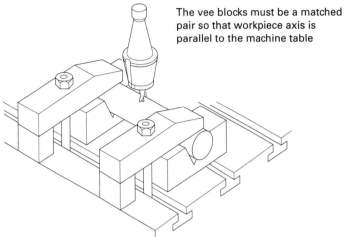

The vee blocks must be a matched pair so that workpiece axis is parallel to the machine table

Clamped on two vee blocks on a vertical milling machine's table

Fixtures

Useful extensively when successive components are to be machined in the same way, i.e. large batch production. A fixture is expensive to produce but provides consistent workpiece location.

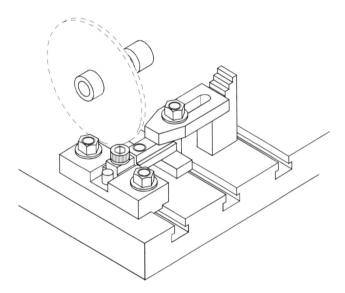

Using a fixture to cut off tee nuts to length

Indexing device

Indexing devices

Used for mounting workpieces which need to be rotated through an angle. Various types of indexing devices are manufactured, a simple indexing unit fitted with a three-jaw self-centring chuck is shown here. It can be mounted on the machine's table with the workpiece along the table's axis or with the workpiece's axis vertical.

Other indexing devices are dividing heads and rotary tables.

Vertical milling attachment for horizontal milling machine

For versatility, some horizontal milling machines can be converted to a vertical milling machine by fitting a vertical attachment.

The vertical milling attachment fits on a horizontal milling machine's column and receives its drive from the spindle nose.

Its tools are mounted in the same way as they would be in a vertical milling machine.

Vertical milling attachments can be tilted over at an angle like the head on a turret mill. This enables the machine to be used in a wide variety of situations.

Exercise 4.5   *Turning tool holder*

Make the turning tool holder using either a vertical or a horizontal milling machine. List the appropriate procedure and tools required. Your finished workpiece should be within the drawing limits.

On completion of the task, carefully measure your work and write in the table the actual sizes, noting any errors.

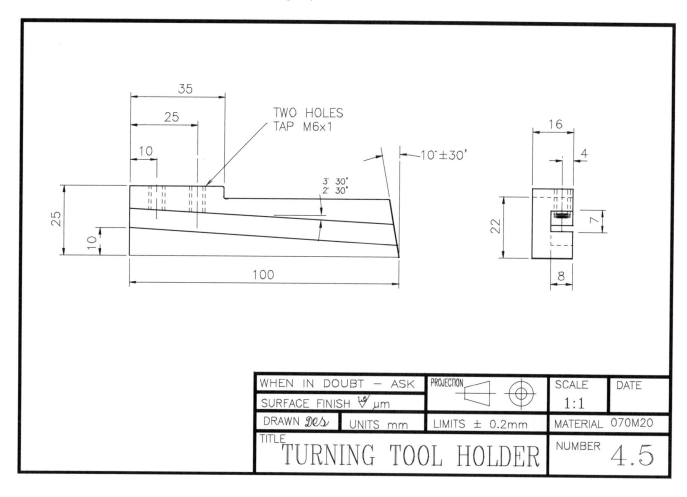

WHEN IN DOUBT — ASK	PROJECTION		SCALE 1:1	DATE
SURFACE FINISH μm				
DRAWN *Des*	UNITS mm	LIMITS ± 0.2mm	MATERIAL 070M20	
TITLE TURNING TOOL HOLDER			NUMBER 4.5	

Planning

Procedure
1 Acquire material and check for size
2
3
4
5
6
7
8
9
10
11 Isolate machine from electrical supply
12 Clean the machine and the work area

Tools and equipment selected

Complete the tables with correct information.

		Reasons for selection
Machine type selected:		**1**
		2
Work-holding device selected		**1**
		2
Cutting tools selected		**1**
1	**3**	**2**
2	**4**	**3**

Write here the checks made on cutting tools before starting work.

1

2

3

Write here the procedure for reporting defective cutters in your workplace.

1

2

Sketch

Draw two sketches to show alternative methods of how the 10° end of the turning tool holder could be held for machining in two different work-holding devices.

Finished inspection report

Component dimensions (mm)	Limits	Actual size	Error
Overall length 100	100·2 99·8		
Slot width 7	7·2 6·8		
Body height 22	22·2 21·8		
Slot depth 8	8·2 7·8		
Slot angle 3°	3° 30' 2° 30'		
Remarks			

Results

Is the workpiece to the drawing specification?   **Yes**   **No**

If the completed workpiece is below drawing specification, write here the reasons for any errors, stating clearly how the errors will be avoided in future.

Start date	End date	Time taken (hours)	Signed satisfactory by supervisor

Exercise 4.6 *Basic milling test*

The multiple choice question paper will only be issued to candidates by their supervisor on satisfactory completion of the appropriate exercises. The answer sheet below must be completed by the candidate when the questions are issued.

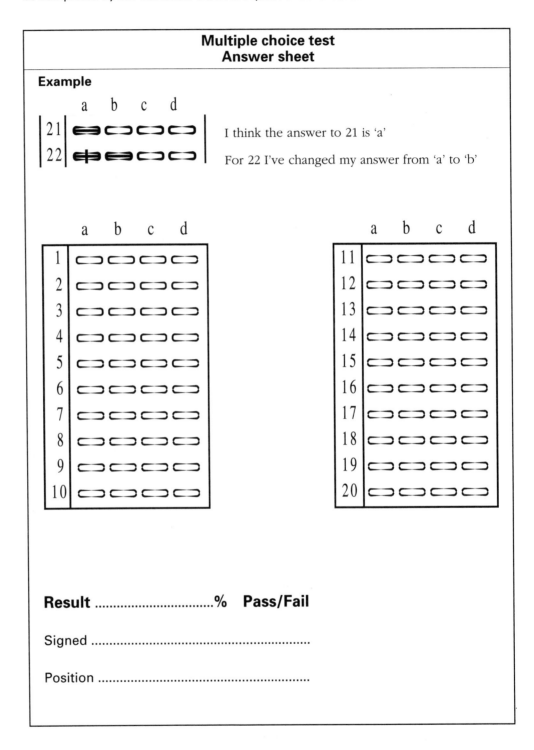

Appendix I
Millimetre to inch conversions

mm	inch	mm	inch	mm	inch	mm	inch	mm	inch
0.01	0.0004	7	0.2756	31	1.2205	55	2.1654	79	3.1102
0.02	0.0008	8	0.3150	32	1.2598	56	2.2047	80	3.1496
0.03	0.0012	9	0.3543	33	1.2992	57	2.2441	81	3.1890
0.04	0.0016	10	0.3937	34	1.3386	58	2.2835	82	3.2283
0.05	0.0020	11	0.4331	35	1.3780	59	2.3228	83	3.2677
0.06	0.0024	12	0.4724	36	1.4173	60	2.3622	84	3.3071
0.07	0.0028	13	0.5118	37	1.4567	61	2.4016	85	3.3465
0.08	0.0032	14	0.5512	38	1.4961	62	2.4409	86	3.3858
0.09	0.0035	15	0.5906	39	1.5354	63	2.4803	87	3.4252
0.1	0.0039	16	0.6299	40	1.5748	64	2.5197	88	3.4646
0.2	0.0079	17	0.6693	41	1.6142	65	2.5591	89	3.5039
0.3	0.0118	18	0.7087	42	1.6535	66	2.5984	90	3.5433
0.4	0.0158	19	0.7480	43	1.6929	67	2.6378	91	3.5827
0.5	0.0197	20	0.7874	44	1.7323	68	2.6772	92	3.6220
0.6	0.0236	21	0.8268	45	1.7717	69	2.7165	93	3.6614
0.7	0.0276	22	0.8661	46	1.8110	70	2.7559	94	3.7008
0.8	0.0315	23	0.9055	47	1.8504	71	2.7953	95	3.7402
0.9	0.0354	24	0.9559	48	1.8898	72	2.8346	96	3.7795
1	0.0394	25	0.9843	49	1.9291	73	2.8740	97	3.8189
2	0.0787	26	1.0236	50	1.9685	74	2.9134	98	3.8583
3	0.1181	27	1.0630	51	2.0079	75	2.9528	99	3.8976
4	0.1575	28	1.1024	52	2.0472	76	2.9921	100	3.9370
5	0.1969	29	1.1417	53	2.0866	77	3.0315	250	9.8430
6	0.2362	30	1.1811	54	2.1260	78	3.0709	1000	39.370

Example

To find the inch equivalent of 27.56 mm

0.06 mm = 0.0024 in
0.5 mm = 0.0197 in
27 mm = 1.0630 in
Total = 1.0851 in

Inch to millimetre conversions

Fractional inch	Decimal inch	mm	Fractional inch	Decimal inch	mm	Fractional inch	Decimal inch	mm
–	0.001	0.0254	–	0.2	5.080	5/8	0.6250	15.88
–	0.002	0.0508	13/64	0.2031	5.16	41/64	0.6406	16.27
–	0.003	0.0762	7/32	0.2188	5.56	21/32	0.6562	16.67
–	0.004	0.1016	15/64	0.2344	5.95	43/64	0.6719	17.07
–	0.005	0.1270	1/4	0.2500	6.35	11/16	0.6875	17.46
–	0.006	0.1524	17/64	0.2656	6.75	–	0.7	17.780
–	0.007	0.1778	9/32	0.2813	7.14	45/64	0.7031	17.86
–	0.008	0.2032	19/64	0.2969	7.54	23/32	0.7188	18.26
–	0.009	0.2286	–	0.3	7.620	47/64	0.7344	18.65
–	0.01	0.254	5/16	0.3125	7.94	3/4	0.7500	19.05
1/64	0.0156	0.39	21/64	0.3281	8.33	49/64	0.7656	19.45
–	0.02	0.508	11/32	0.3438	8.73	25/32	0.7813	19.84
–	0.03	0.762	23/64	0.3594	9.13	51/64	0.7969	20.24
1/32	0.0312	0.79	3/8	0.3750	9.53	–	0.8	20.320
–	0.04	1.016	25/64	0.3906	9.92	13/16	0.8125	20.64
3/64	0.0469	1.19	–	0.4	10.160	53/64	0.8281	21.03
–	0.05	1.270	13/32	0.4063	10.32	27/32	0.8438	21.43
–	0.06	1.524	27/64	0.4219	10.72	55/64	0.8594	21.83
1/16	0.0625	1.59	7/16	0.4375	11.11	7/8	0.8750	22.23
	0.07	1.778	29/64	0.4531	11.51	57/64	0.8906	22.62
5/64	0.0781	1.98	15/32	0.4688	11.90	–	0.9	22.860
–	0.08	2.032	31/64	0.4844	12.30	29/32	0.9063	23.02
–	0.09	2.286	1/2 (0.5)	0.5000	12.70	59/64	0.9219	24.42
3/32	0.0938	2.38	33/64	0.5156	13.10	15/16	0.9375	23.81
–	0.1	2.540	17/32	0.5312	13.49	61/64	0.9531	24.21
7/64	0.1093	2.78	35/64	0.5469	13.89	31/32	0.9688	24.61
1/8	0.1250	3.18	9/16	0.5625	14.29	63/64	0.9844	25.00
9/64	0.1406	3.57	37/64	0.5781	14.68	1	1.0000	25.40
5/32	0.1563	3.97	19/32	0.5938	15.08	2	2.0000	50.80
11/64	0.1719	4.37	–	0.6	15.240	5	5.0000	127.00
3/16	0.1875	4.76	39/64	0.6094	15.48	10	10.000	254.00

Tapping sizes for common threads

The tapping sizes in this chart are for standard threads only

ISO Metric Thread angle 60°			BSW (Whitworth) Thread angle 55°			BSF (British Standard Fine) Thread angle 55°		
Major dia.	Pitch (mm)	Tapping size (mm)	Major dia (in)	Pitch (tpi)	Tapping size (mm)	Major dia.	Pitch (tpi)	Tapping size (mm)
M4 × 0.7		3.3	1/8	40	2.55	-	-	-
M5 × 0.8		4.2	3/16	24	3.7	3/16	32	4.0
M6 × 1.0		5.0	1/4	20	5.1	1/4	26	5.3
M7 × 1.0		6.0	5/16	18	6.5	5/16	22	6.8
M8 × 1.25		6.8	3/8	16	7.9	3/8	20	8.3
M10 × 1.5		8.5	7/16	14	9.3	7/16	18	9.7
M12 × 1.75		10.2	1/2	12	10.5	1/2	16	11.1
M14 × 2		12.0	9/16	12	12.0	9/16	16	14.0
M16 × 2		14.0	5/8	11	13.5	5/8	14	12.6

BA (British Association) Thread angle 47.5°			UNC (Unified Coarse) Thread angle 60°			UNF (Unified Fine) Thread angle 60°		
Designation	Pitch (tpi)	Tapping size (mm)	Major dia.	Pitch (tpi)	Tapping size (mm)	Major dia.	Pitch (tpi)	Tapping size (mm)
0	25.4	5.0	1/4	20	5.2	1/4	28	5.4
1	28.2	4.4	5/16	18	6.5	5/16	24	6.8
2	31.3	4.0	3/8	16	8	3/8	24	8.4
3	34.8	3.3	7/16	14	9.3	7/16	20	9.8
4	38.5	2.95	1/2	13	10.8	1/2	20	11.4
5	43.1	2.6	9/16	12	12.1	9/16	18	12.8
6	47.9	2.25	5/8	11	13.5	5/8	18	14.5

The sizes of the tapping drills listed above are the nearest convenient size larger than the threads' core diameters
If you need to use an alternative drill use the next larger size

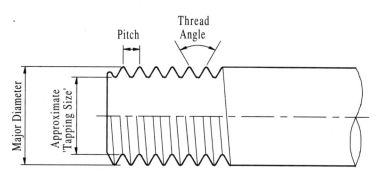

Drill speeds and feeds

1. Drill spindle speeds

Drill diameter (mm)	Aluminium	Brass	Cast iron	Bronze	Mild steel	High carbon steel	Hard alloy steel
up to 3	5250	4800	850	3000	2500	2000	950
4 – 8	1600	2400	450	1500	1250	1000	475
8 – 10	2000	2000	310	1200	950	650	325
10 – 14	1400	1250	220	800	650	475	250
14 – 20	950	880	150	550	450	350	175
20 – 30	750	640	100	400	325	225	120
30 – 50	500	400	60	250	200	150	75

The above spindle speeds should only be set if your cutting conditions are ideal
i.e. if you have sharp tools, cutting fluid, secure clamping and a rigid machine tool

2. Drill feed rates

Drill diameter (mm)	Feed rate (mm/rev)	Feed (in/rev)
up to 3	0·05	0·002
4 – 8	0·06	0·003
8 – 10	0·15	0·006
10 – 14	0·20	0·008
14 – 20	0·30	0·012
20 – 30	0·40	0·016
30 – 50	0·50	0·020

The above feed rates should only be set if your cutting conditions are ideal
i.e. if you have sharp tools, cutting fluid available, secure clamping and a rigid machine tool
If your conditions are not ideal, use a slower speed

Example   *When setting up to drill a ø12 hole in cast iron, the spindle speed should be set at 220 rev/min and the feed rate should be set at 0·2 mm/rev (0·008 in/rev)*

Reaming allowances

Finished diameter (mm)	Drill size for machine reaming	Drill size for hand reaming
Up to 8	Hole size minus 0·25 mm	Hole size minus 0·2 mm
over 8 up to 12	Hole size minus 0·3 mm	Hole size minus 0·25 mm
over 12 up to 18	Hole size minus 0·4 mm	Hole size minus 0·35 mm
over 18 up to 25	Hole size minus 0·6 mm	Hole size minus 0·5 mm
Over 25	Hole size minus 0·75 mm	Hole size minus 0·6 mm

Spindle speeds for reaming should be set at approximately half the equivalent drill speed

Feed rates for reaming should be approximately twice the equivalent drill feed

Tips on reaming

1. Ensure workpiece is held tightly.
2. Drill correct size hole before reaming.
3. Use cutting fluid or lubricant.
4. Ream straight after drilling and without moving the workpiece.
5. Select recommended speeds and feeds.
6. Look after the ream to maintain sharp cutting edges.
7. Continue to turn reamer forwards when withdrawing from workpiece.

Example

1. *The pilot drill size for hand reaming a ø8 mm hole*   8 − 0·2 = 7·8 mm
2. *The pilot drill size for machine reaming a ø20 mm hole*   20 − 0·6 = 19·4 mm

Torque wrench settings

The table below is guidance for torque wrench settings, use it only if manufacturers' recommended torque settings are not available.

Metric thread size	Torque wrench setting (n/m)		
	4·6 quality	8·8 quality	12·9 quality
M4 x 0·7	1·3	3· 5	6
M5 x 0·8	2·7	7·1	12
M6 x 1	4·5	12·1	20·4
M8 x 1·25	11	29·4	49·6
M10 x 1·5	21·8	58·3	98
M12 x 1·75	38·1	102	171
M14 x 2	60·6	162	273
M16 x 2	95	252	426
M20 x 2·5	185	492	830

Imperial thread size	Torque wrench setting (lbf/ft)		
	'R' quality	'S' quality	'X' quality
$\frac{1}{4}$ Whit	8·2	9·1	15
$\frac{5}{16}$ Whit	17	19	31
$\frac{3}{8}$ Whit	30	33	55
$\frac{7}{16}$ Whit	48	53	88
$\frac{1}{2}$ Whit	70	79	130
$\frac{1}{4}$ BSF	9·1	9·1	17
$\frac{5}{16}$ BSF	18	19	33
$\frac{3}{8}$ BSF	32	33	59
$\frac{7}{16}$ BSF	51	53	95
$\frac{1}{2}$ BSF	77	82	143
$\frac{1}{4}$ UNC	8·2	10	15
$\frac{5}{16}$ UNC	17	20	31
$\frac{3}{8}$ UNC	30	36	55
$\frac{7}{16}$ UNC	48	58	89
$\frac{1}{2}$ UNC	73	86	136
$\frac{1}{4}$ UNF	9·3	10	17
$\frac{5}{16}$ UNF	19	21	34
$\frac{3}{8}$ UNF	34	36	63
$\frac{7}{16}$ UNF	53	60	99
$\frac{1}{2}$ UNF	82	91	152

Spindle speeds for turning and milling

To calculate the correct spindle speed for a machining operation, it is necessary to make a calculation using the formula shown below. The calculated revolutions per minute should be accepted *only* as nominal. Adjustments to this calculated speed can be made to determine the optimum speed during the component manufacture. Remember that if there is no cutting fluid or coolant available the speed should be reduced.

$$\text{Rev/min} = \frac{1000 \times S}{\pi \times d}$$

Where S = Cutting speed of the work material
d = Work (or tool) diameter
π = 3.142

This table shows the recommended cutting speeds (values for S) in metres per minute for some common engineering materials.

Material	Cutting speed
Aluminium	60 m/min
Brass	45 m/min
Cast iron	25 m/min
Bronze	30 m/min
Mild steel	25 m/min
High carbon steel	18 m/min
Hard alloy steel	10 m/min

Note When using tungsten tools multiply the above values by 2

The above cutting speeds should be only be used if your cutting conditions are ideal
i.e. if you have sharp tools, cutting fluid available, secure clamping and a rigid machine tool
If your conditions are not ideal, use a slower speed

Example 1   *To **turn** a mild steel bar of diameter ø20 mm with HSS tooling, the spindle speed would be calculated as:*

$$\text{Rev/min} = \frac{1000 \times S}{\pi \times d}$$

Where S = Cutting speed of the work material
= 25 m/min
d = Work diameter
= 20 mm
π = 3.142
= Approximately 3

$$\text{Rev/min} = \frac{1000 \times 25}{3 \times 20}$$

= 416 rev/min

Example 2   *To **Mill** high carbon steel with a ø125 mm HSS cutter, the spindle speed would be calculated as:*

$$\text{Rev/min} = \frac{1000 \times S}{\pi \times d}$$

Where S = Cutting speed of the work material
= 18 m/min
d = Tool diameter
= 125 mm
π = 3.142
= Approximately 3

$$\text{Rev/min} = \frac{1000 \times 18}{3 \times 125}$$

= 48 rev/min

Feed rates for milling

The feed rates given in this table are recommended feed rates for sharp HSS cutters working on robust machinery and using correct coolants/cutting fluids. They are correct for all materials. If in any doubt about feed rates always use a slower one than calculated.

The suggested feed rates are based on 1 x cutter diameter of axial cut depth and $\frac{1}{2}$ cutter diameter for radial depth of cut.

Feed rates for end mills and slot drills

Cutter dia. (mm)	Feed per tooth (mm) for end mills	Feed per tooth (mm) for slot drills
2	0·0075 – 0·013	0·013
3	0·013 – 0·025	0·018
6	0·025 – 0·037	0·025
12	0·037 – 0·050	0·050
25	0·05 – 0·064	0·090
50	0·064 – 0·075	0·013

Table feed per minute = Feed per tooth x no of teeth on cutter x rev per min of cutting tool

Feed/min = feed/tooth x no of teeth x rev/min

The above feed rates should be only be set if your cutting conditions are ideal
i.e. if you have sharp tools, cutting fluid available, secure clamping and a rigid machine tool
If your conditions are not ideal, use a slower feed

Example 1 *For end milling a brass workpiece with a high-speed steel four-tooth ø25 end mill, the feed rate would be found as follows:*

(a) Work out spindle speed:

$$\text{Rev/min} = \frac{1000 \times S}{\pi \times d}$$

= 600 rev/min

(b) Calculate feed rate:

Feed/min = feed/tooth x no of teeth x rev/min
= 0.05 x 4 x 600
= 120 mm/min

Example 2 *For slot drilling a 12 mm wide slot in aluminium using a high speed-steel slot drill, the feed rate would be found as follows:*

(a) Work out spindle speed:

$$\text{Rev/min} = \frac{1000 \times S}{\pi \times d}$$

= 1666 rev/min

(b) Calculate feed rate:

Feed/min = feed/tooth x no of teeth x rev/min
= 0.05 x 2 x 1666
= 166.7 mm/min

Repeat test

The multiple choice question paper will only be issued to candidates by their supervisor on satisfactory completion of the appropriate exercises. The answer sheet below must be completed by the candidate when the questions are issued.

**Multiple choice test
Answer sheet**

Example

	a	b	c	d	
21	⊟	⊏⊐	⊏⊐	⊏⊐	I think the answer to 21 is 'a'
22	⊞	⊟	⊏⊐	⊏⊐	For 22 I've changed my answer from 'a' to 'b'

	a	b	c	d
1	⊏⊐	⊏⊐	⊏⊐	⊏⊐
2	⊏⊐	⊏⊐	⊏⊐	⊏⊐
3	⊏⊐	⊏⊐	⊏⊐	⊏⊐
4	⊏⊐	⊏⊐	⊏⊐	⊏⊐
5	⊏⊐	⊏⊐	⊏⊐	⊏⊐
6	⊏⊐	⊏⊐	⊏⊐	⊏⊐
7	⊏⊐	⊏⊐	⊏⊐	⊏⊐
8	⊏⊐	⊏⊐	⊏⊐	⊏⊐
9	⊏⊐	⊏⊐	⊏⊐	⊏⊐
10	⊏⊐	⊏⊐	⊏⊐	⊏⊐

	a	b	c	d
11	⊏⊐	⊏⊐	⊏⊐	⊏⊐
12	⊏⊐	⊏⊐	⊏⊐	⊏⊐
13	⊏⊐	⊏⊐	⊏⊐	⊏⊐
14	⊏⊐	⊏⊐	⊏⊐	⊏⊐
15	⊏⊐	⊏⊐	⊏⊐	⊏⊐
16	⊏⊐	⊏⊐	⊏⊐	⊏⊐
17	⊏⊐	⊏⊐	⊏⊐	⊏⊐
18	⊏⊐	⊏⊐	⊏⊐	⊏⊐
19	⊏⊐	⊏⊐	⊏⊐	⊏⊐
20	⊏⊐	⊏⊐	⊏⊐	⊏⊐

Result ....% **Pass/Fail**

Signed ....

Position ....

Index

A

alignment of lathe centres 85
Allen keys (hexagon socket
    wrenches) 44
angle cutter 133
angle plate 12, 146
angular work, setting (milling) 124–6
apron 4
apron (of lathe saddle) 61
arbor 131, 134
    mounting 135
    stub arbor 139, 140

B

barrier cream 4
bed 61
bench 7
bench drilling machine 18
bench fitting 6–58
boring on a centre lathe 90–92
built up edge 77, 145

C

carriage 61
catch plate 83, 84, 85
centre drill 22
centre drilling 78
centre lathe 59–63
    sizes of 62
    work holding devices 63, 82–4
    cutting tool shapes 64, 100
    spindle speed selection 64, 158
    setting the cutting tool 66
    spindle nose 60
centre lathe turning 59–108
chamfering 72, 75
chemicals 3, 4
chisels (cold chisels) 54
    using chisels 54
    point angles 54–5
    grinding 54
climb (down cut) milling 118
collars (on milling arbor) 140
column 111, 131
column and knee milling
    machines 109–10, 130
compound slide 61
    taper turning 86
concentric 93, 84, 118
convex/concave cutter 133
coolant 67

counterbore 24
countersink 24
cross slide (centre lathe) 61
cutting fluid 67

D

defects on cutting tools 77, 145
    reporting 145
dermatitis 4
dial test indicator (DTI) 114, 114–15
die stock 32
dies 31
    circular split 32
    die nut 32
    using dies 32, 72
    care of 33
double cut files 9
drawbar 117, 135
drill chuck 24
drill drift 25
drill guards 19, 26
drilling
    on bench drilling machine 19
    on a pillar drill 26
    on a lathe 78–9
dust mask 4

E

ear defenders 3
ear plugs 3
electrical interlocks 119

F

face plate 82
facing on a centre lathe 75, 62
feed direction 119
feed rate selection
    milling 159, 118
    drilling 155
feedrate (for turning) 67
files 8–10
    care of 13
    shape 10
    length 8, 10
    selecting 9
    handles 8
    grade 9
    cuts 9
    card 13
    using 10

filing techniques 11–12
    straight filing 11
    drawfiling 11
    filing flat 11
    filing square 12
    finishing 12
    curves 11
fitter 6
fixed abutments 140
fixture 147
four-jaw chuck 82, 104–5
    work setting 104

G

gangways 4
gloves
    leather 3, 117, 135
    thermal 3
    rubber 5
guards
    chuck 67, 68
    bellows type (centre lathe) 68
    drill 19
    vertical milling 119–20
    horizontal milling 136

H

hacksaw
    blade 16
    blade selection 16–17
    using 17
    junior hacksaw 18
    care of 18
hair net 3
hammers 51
hat 3
headstock (centre lathe) 60
Health and Safety at Work Act 1974 1, 2,
    4, 68, 119, 136
helmet 3
hexagon socket wrenches 44
hole cutting tools 22–5
    drills 22
    centre drill 22
    twist drill 23
    reamer 23, 24
    countersink 24
    counterbore 24
horizontal milling machine 130–32
hygiene procedures 4

I

indexing devices 147–8

K

key (for locating milling cutter) 135
knee 110, 111, 131

knurling 97–8, 63
knurling tools 97

L

lathe carriers 85
lathe stops 93
lathe tools
    angles 76
    materials 76
    defects 77
    boring 90
lifting technique 84

M

machine centres 65
machine tapping head 99
machine vices 113–15
machining slots 126
mandrel 93
mandrel press 93
measuring bores 92
milling 109–51
milling cutters (horizontal)
    slab mill 132
    side and face cutter 132
    slotting cutter 133
    slitting saw 133
    form cutters (angle and radius
        cutters) 133
    shell end mill 116, 134
    face mill 117, 134
    mounting 134–6
    defects on 144
milling cutters (vertical)
    end mill 116
    slot drill 116
    shell end mill 116
    face mill 117
    ball nose cutter 116
    dovetail cutter 116
    tee slot cutter 116
    ripping cutter 116
    mounting cutters in milling
        chucks 117–18
milling machine sizes 112, 131
morse taper 25
    shank drills 23, 78
mounting lathe cutting tools
    tailstock 78
    tool post 66
mounting workpieces in a vice 115–16
mushrooming (of chisels) 54, 55

O

overalls 2
overarm 131

P

parting off 100, 63
parting off tool 100
pein (of a hammer) 51
pillar drilling machine 25
pipe wrench 48
plain horizontal milling machine 130
pliers, selecting and using 47
point angles (of fitters' tools) 55
protective clothing 2

R

reamers
  hand 23
  machine 24
reaming 39–40
  by hand 40
  by machine 40, 79
reaming allowances 156
respirator 4
riveting 51–2

S

saddle
  centre lathe 61
  milling 111, 131
safety 1
  glasses 3
  boots 2–3
  precautions and procedures 1
  glasses 3
  helmet 3
screwdrivers 43
shaping machine 36
side and face cutter 140, 133
slab mill 130
slitting saw 130
slot drilling 126
slotting cutter 130
socket set 45
spanners 44–5
speed selection
  milling 118, 158
  turning 158,
  drilling 18, 115
spindle
  lathe 60
  milling 111, 131
spotfacing tool 24
spring collets 83
stillson (pipe wrench) 48
storing materials 4
straddle milling 140
stub arbor 139
  fitting 140

T

table (milling) 112, 131
tailstock 61
tap wrench 30
taper turning (compound slide) 86
tapping
  sizes 154
  by hand 29, 30
  on a lathe
    by hand 98
    machine 99
  compound 30, 41
taps
  hand 30
  machine 99
  care of 31
tenons 114
threads
  cutting external 31, 32, 72
  cutting internal 29–30, 98
  checking 33
three-jaw chuck 82
tool post (centre lathe) 66, 61
torque wrench 45
  settings 46, 157
  using 46
try square 12
turning between centres 84
turret 111
turret milling machine 111

U

universal milling machine 130–31
up cut milling 118

V

vee blocks 147
vertical milling attachment 148
vertical milling machine 110
vice
  bench 7
  machine 113, 124, 125
vice jaws
  bench vice 7
  pull down type (for machine vice) 114

W

work holding devices
  lathe 82–4
  changing 84
  milling machine 112–14, 145–8
work holding vices (milling) 112–16

Y

yoke 131, 134